THE
ILLUSTRATED ENCYCLOPAEDIA
OF ANIMAL LIFE

THE ANIMAL KINGDOM

The strange and wonderful ways of
mammals, birds, reptiles, fishes and
insects. A new and authentic natural
history of the wild life of the world

VOLUME 11

FREDERICK DRIMMER, M.A.
EDITOR-IN-CHIEF

GEORGE G. GOODWIN
Associate Curator of Mammals,
The American Museum of Natural
History

CHARLES M. BOGERT
Curator of Amphibians and Reptiles,
The American Museum of Natural
History

DEAN AMADON
E. THOMAS GILLIARD
Associate Curators of Birds,
The American Museum of Natural History

CHRISTOPHER W. COATES *Curator*
JAMES W. ATZ *Assistant Curator*
Aquarium of The New York Zoological
Society

JOHN C. PALLISTER
Research Associate, Insects, The American Museum of Natural History

ODHAMS BOOKS LIMITED, LONG ACRE, LONDON

Colour photographs supplied by members of The Free Lance Photographers Guild except as otherwise individually credited.

——PARASITES ON THE BOX TURTLE. More subtle in their aggressions, if not so deadly, are the parasites that infest box turtles. Ewing found some turtles in Maryland covered with the larvae of the common American chigger, the pernicious mite that occasionally causes severe irritation on the skin of human beings. Even more insidious are the infestations of the turtle flesh flies. These insects deposit their larvae on the soft parts of the turtles, where the grubs bore their way into the skin. Here they grow at the painful expense of the turtle. When grown and perhaps a quarter of an inch wide, the grubs emerge and fall on the ground, leaving a hole in the host's body. Here they burrow into the earth to pupate before they appear as adult flies.

——BOX TURTLES AS PETS. Relatively few turtles are infested in this way. Most box turtles are handsome animals, ideal for observation in captivity. Few reptiles are so easily confined. They should be given water for drinking or soaking, and some moist leaves or rotting vegetation in which to burrow at night. To dig her nest, the female needs sandy soil in direct sunlight. But some shade is necessary, for prolonged exposure to direct sunlight can be fatal to turtles.

——TURTLE TERMINOLOGY. The box turtle is also called a "tortoise", but this name is commonly used only for such land dwellers as the Desert Tortoise, *Gopherus agassizi*, which rarely enters the water. "Terrapin" is another name, of American Indian origin which some

THE DIAMOND BACK TERRAPIN—GOURMET'S DELIGHT

This turtle of the tidal waters of the Atlantic coast of America brings higher prices, pound for pound, than any other turtle. So succulent is its flesh that fashionable hotels have paid almost a hundred dollars a dozen for the terrapin.

use rather loosely. Others would apply the term only to turtles more commonly used for food—the Diamond Back Terrapin, *Malaclemmys terrapin*, for example. These are all turtles, or, more technically, members of the Order Testudinata.

The Slider, *Pseudemys scripta troosti.* Another common inhabitant of streams in the eastern part of the United States is called Troost's Turtle in books, but it is more generally known by the popular name of "slider". The small turtles most often sold in pet shops in America are juvenile sliders, a species that is unbelievably abundant in many parts of the Mississippi Valley, from Illinois southward to Louisiana.

Dr. Fred Cagle, who has made an intensive study of the habits, behaviour, and breeding of the slider turtle, has collected by hand or trapped over eight thousand individuals. He concluded that eight out of every ten turtles inhabiting the fresh waters of Louisiana are sliders. Thousands upon thousands are sent annually from Louisiana to pet shops throughout the United States. Some of these are hatchlings from eggs incubated under artificial conditions. Cagle reports that three collectors dug more than three thousand eggs from nests in a railroad embankment in a single afternoon. Such incredible inroads may eventually reduce the numbers of sliders in the immediate region of the raids. Thus far, however, there has been no perceptible reduction in the turtle populations.

Sliders, so called from their habit of sliding into the water upon the approach of an intruder, live mostly in the water. They feed there habitually, ordinarily venturing on land only to breed or to bask except during the spring and late summer. During these times of the year there are overland migrations that probably account for the presence of sliders in all suitable waters within their range.

——THE SLIDER'S APPEARANCE. Except for old males, sliders are rather flat, greenish-coloured turtles with yellowish streaks on their heads and necks. Their most characteristic marking, however, is a bright red line that extends from behind the eyes to the back of the head. The male matures in from two to five years, when its plastron, the bottom part of its shell, is three and one-half to four inches long. The female is not ready to breed until her plastron is from six to eight inches long.

Apart from being much smaller than the female, the male is easily distinguished because its front claws are twice as long as its hind ones.

THE
ILLUSTRATED ENCYCLOPAEDIA
OF ANIMAL LIFE

THE ANIMAL KINGDOM

The strange and wonderful ways of
mammals, birds, reptiles, fishes and
insects. A new and authentic natural
history of the wild life of the world

VOLUME 11

FREDERICK DRIMMER, M.A.
EDITOR-IN-CHIEF

GEORGE G. GOODWIN
*Associate Curator of Mammals,
The American Museum of Natural
History*

CHARLES M. BOGERT
*Curator of Amphibians and Reptiles,
The American Museum of Natural
History*

DEAN AMADON
E. THOMAS GILLIARD
*Associate Curators of Birds,
The American Museum of Natural History*

CHRISTOPHER W. COATES *Curator*
JAMES W. ATZ *Assistant Curator*
*Aquarium of The New York Zoological
Society*

JOHN C. PALLISTER
Research Associate, Insects, The American Museum of Natural History

ODHAMS BOOKS LIMITED, LONG ACRE, LONDON

Colour photographs supplied by members of The Free Lance Photographers Guild except as otherwise individually credited.

In females the front and hind claws are about the same length. Unfortunately these differences hold only for adults; there are no external characteristics that enable us to determine the sex of the juveniles sold in pet shops.

The female undergoes no conspicuous change in colour while she is growing. But the male frequently becomes increasingly blacker in its old age until it is almost impossible to discern any markings whatsoever. The two sexes are so strikingly different that for decades naturalists believed the black males represented a distinct species. Now that they have observed the courtship, there is no question concerning the identity of the two. Moreover, the purpose of the long claws on the male has become apparent.

——COURTSHIP AMONG THE SLIDER TURTLES. During the spring or autumn the male pursues the female, repeatedly swimming in front of her and facing her. Sometimes three or four males will court a female at the same time. Eventually one of them manages to get himself in the proper position. There in front of the female, the male draws his forelimbs together and vibrates his claws against her head. If she is receptive, she swims along slowly, allowing the male to continue to stroke her chin and cheeks as he swims along backwards. Finally she sinks to the bottom, with the male in pursuit. The pair complete their courtship while they are on the bottom, often in water so deep that an observer has difficulty in watching them.

——FROM EGG TO ADULT. The female slider lays from one to three clutches of eggs between April and the middle of July. Each clutch may contain from four to twenty eggs, depending on the turtle's size. In order to deposit her eggs the female leaves the water to seek an open spot where the soil is not muddy. Sometimes the turtle chooses the summit of a hill; often she must travel several miles to find a suitable nesting site. She digs out a jug-shaped hole with her hind legs, and if the ground is hard she releases fluid from her bladder to soften it. Cagle reports that some turtles need more than three hours to dig the nest, whereas others succeed in less than half an hour. Owing to the turtle's shyness, however, Cagle never succeeded in watching the actual laying of the eggs.

The eggs hatch throughout the summer, from July to late September. Those in individual clutches require from sixty-eight to seventy days, depending upon the temperature of the nest. The eggs vary in size but average an inch and one-half in length and seven-eighths of an inch in width. When the hatchling is ready to emerge it cuts one end of the egg, using either the temporary "egg breaker" on its snout or its front claws; sometimes both the tooth and the claws are used. Upon emerging the hatchling is approximately an inch and a quarter long.

Like the young of the box turtle, those of the slider do not always come out of the nest when they have hatched. They may spend the entire winter in the nest, relying upon the large yolk mass to sustain them. Once they start to feed, however, their growth is quite rapid. Cagle found that there were annual increases in the plastron length varying from about half an inch to as much as one and one-half inches. Adults tend to grow more slowly, and in old age finally remain at a fixed size. A female with a carapace fourteen and one-half inches long is considered large, although a sixteen-inch specimen has been reported from Michigan.

——FOOD AND FOES. The slider eats almost anything, showing no special preference for animal or plant food. In its natural surroundings in Illinois it eats tadpoles, molluscs, crayfish, insect larvae, as well as small fish. In captivity it will take almost any food offered to it, including vegetables, fruits, and water plants. In Texas a naturalist fed captives on a diet of meat, grasshoppers, and fish.

In the northern part of its range, the slider has few natural enemies once it has reached the adult stage. But along the Gulf Coast the alligator and the giant garfish take a significant toll. Cagle states that crows sometimes destroy numbers of turtles when the turtles first emerge from hibernation. In Illinois he frightened crows away from sluggish turtles lying on the bank of a stream, and found that some had been turned on their backs by the wily birds. The crows had pecked a hole into the body cavity just in front of the hind legs, the vulnerable spot on most turtles.

During the winter in Illinois Cagle found a few turtles with their shells gnawed by muskrats. Both mink and otter capture and devour a few, and Cagle says that raccoons have been seen ripping the eggs from a female slider seeking a nesting site. Fishermen in some areas destroy these turtles in the mistaken belief that they are harmful to fish, although it is doubtful whether any game fish are eaten in sizable quantities by the slider.

As so often proves to be the case with other animals, man is probably this turtle's greatest enemy. Countless thousands, as mentioned above, are sold as pets. Many hatchlings are disfigured with paint before they reach the market. Such unfortunate turtles inevitably become malformed because the paint, unless it is removed, interferes with their growth.

In Tennessee thousands of eggs are dug up each year to be sold as fish bait. Skunks, raccoons and snakes also take a tremendous toll of eggs.

Cagle estimates that hardly one egg out of ten will survive these raids, especially when nests are concentrated in one area. On a single bank where he counted more than five hundred nests, intensive search revealed only one nest that was still intact.

Obviously the odds in favour of any individual egg's hatching and producing a turtle that is to live until it reaches maturity are exceedingly small. Were it not for the large number of eggs produced, and the great age attained by a few sliders, their numbers would undoubtedly be considerably reduced. No one knows how long these turtles live, but Cagle suggests that a female fortunate enough to escape its enemies might well continue to lay eggs over a period of forty to fifty years.

——Sliders as Pets. Sliders are able to remain active between temperatures of 60° and 95° Fahrenheit, but they probably prefer temperatures between 75° and 80°. Pets can be kept at such temperatures in an aquarium, where some object should be provided to allow them to come out of the water. Unless turtles have sunlight for basking, however, they do not thrive. Chopped meat, fish, earthworms, or tender, fresh vegetables will serve as food. Cod-liver oil smeared on the meat before it is offered will offset deficiencies in the diet, and possibly counteract the lack of sunlight from which turtles kept in urban apartments often suffer. Some commercial preparations sold as "ant eggs" do not provide a suitable diet for turtles.

——The Slider's Relatives. The slider has several close relatives that differ from it in coloration and probably in habits. The eastern race or subspecies is known as the Yellow-bellied Turtle, *Pseudemys scripta scripta*. It inhabits streams and ponds along the Atlantic Coast of the United States from North Carolina to northern Florida, and westward along the Gulf Coast to eastern Louisiana, where it gradually merges with the slider. The yellow-bellied turtle has a yellow blotch, instead of the red streak, behind its eyes. If one were to collect turtles along this coast, capturing some in every river he encountered, he would discover that some turtles in western Florida were intermediate between sliders and yellow-bellied turtles, with characteristics of each.

Farther west, the slider gives way to a whole series of populations that range down the east coast to Mexico and on through Central America to Panama. Another series of populations inhabits the rivers on the west coast of Mexico, ranging as far north as Sonora. One branch of the same stock crossed the Gulf of California to reach the southern end of the peninsula of Lower California. The turtles in each area differ slightly from those in nearby regions. Yet the differences are sometimes so slight that turtles from one area might well interbreed with those on either side of it. Thus they are all called subspecies of a single wide-ranging species, which bears the name of the first one described. In this instance it happens to be *scripta* of the Atlantic Coast.

The Giant Tortoise, *Testudo elephantopus*. The tortoises include some of the bulkiest of the land-dwelling reptiles that still survive. Among the more famous are those inhabiting the Galápagos Islands off the coast of Ecuador. Properly speaking, *galápago* is the Spanish term for a freshwater turtle, whereas the giant tortoises are land animals. Whatever the Spaniards may have assumed, their intention was to name the islands for the great land-dwelling chelonians. ("Chelonian", from the Greek, is a general term for tortoises or turtles.) As the tortoises could be kept alive unfed and packed in the ship's hold, they provided unsurpassed supplies of fresh meat for the early buccaneers. Later the whalers who visited the Galápagos region came to rely upon the tortoises for similar purposes, carrying them off by the hundreds.

——Where Giant Tortoises Are Found. In past ages some land-dwelling turtles inhabiting continental mainlands grew to colossal dimensions. A prehistoric one from India was named *Colossochelys* and not without reason. Yet structurally it was little different from present-day giants. But within historic times most of the truly large tortoises have lived on islands. The islands in the Indian Ocean, notably the Seychelles, supported elephantine tortoises at least four feet long. No species, however, was much more spectacular than that living in the Galápagos. There are no reliable records of maximum weights for tortoises from these islands, but it is reasonably certain that some of them weighed upward of five hundred pounds.

We do not know how their ancestors reached the islands, which were never connected to the mainland of South America. Naturalists assume that the ancestral tortoise must have crossed the sea in some accidental manner, possibly clinging to driftwood carried out from a river mouth. Tortoises can float and survive for long periods in sea water. A relatively large tortoise, not too distantly related to the one on the Galápagos, survives on the South American mainland. The island form is certainly derived from the same stock.

THE GALÁPAGOS TURTLE—ISLAND GIANT

In past ages, some turtles grew to spectacular sizes in the relative security of island existence. One of the most remarkable of these island turtles is the Galápagos tortoise, weighing in the neighbourhood of five hundred pounds. For much of their food these huge creatures depend on the sharp-spined cactus, without suffering any ill effects.

In whatever way the ancestral tortoise reached the Galápagos Islands, it also managed to spread throughout the archipelago. Those on individual islands, or in isolated parts of some of the larger islands, developed their own peculiarities. At one time naturalists recognized as many as sixteen species. It is now conceded by more enlightened naturalists that all of these are races of a single species. The juveniles are very similar in appearance, regardless of which population they represent. Moreover, the adults are so variable in shape and proportions that only average differences serve to distinguish them. If there were no natural barriers between populations it is probable that all of them would interbreed.

——THE LIFE OF THE GALÁPAGOS TORTOISE. Very little is known about the life history of the Galápagos tortoise. Years ago, Samuel Garman reported that a female he examined contained only two eggs about ready to be laid. These he described as about the size of a "one pound shot" although one weighed six ounces. They are white-shelled, spherical, and about two and one-half inches in diameter. It is probable that the larger females lay more than two eggs.

In their isolated habitats the giant tortoises apparently fill the niche occupied by the larger vegetarian mammals in continental regions. On the Galápagos Islands tortoises eat grass as well as the sharp-spined cactus—not only the fruits and blossoms, but also the succulent stems. Observers have marvelled that such soft-tongued creatures as tortoises could devour cactus. However, Edmund Heller tells of a specimen that he found with the palate and throat bristling with cactus spines, which had caused no apparent suffering.

Soon after the rainy season the great lumbering reptiles with their elephantine feet descend the mountainous slopes of the islands to feed on the grass-covered flats. After the grass withers during the dry season, they again ascend the slopes to live in the moist meadows. At such times, in the past, they used to congregate in some numbers in the vicinity of springs, although they never voluntarily entered the water.

——ENEMIES OF THE GIANT TORTOISE. Unfortunately the advent of man, who brought cats, dogs, pigs and the inevitable rats with him, has spelled disaster for the Galápagos tortoise. Pigs, and probably the rats and dogs as well, dig up the eggs and devour them. Hundreds of tortoises were killed for the oil that could be rendered from their fatty tissues. In some of the smaller islands, man has already exterminated the tortoises. Even on Albemarle, the largest of the Galápagos Islands, they have become increasingly difficult to find. At present there are a number alive in the zoological gardens of the United States and Europe. Each year sees their numbers dwindle. No one has succeeded in breeding them in captivity, and a few more decades will probably bring about their extinction—due largely to the thoughtlessness of man.

The Desert Tortoise, *Gopherus agassizi.* Like other land-dwelling chelonians, the desert tortoise is a vegetarian. Its food consists of the tasty herbaceous plants that cover the desert for short intervals at the time of the spring or summer rains. During hot, dry periods some individuals aestivate (lie torpid) or seek the seclusion of an underground burrow constructed for the purpose. Others remain abroad, like their Galápagos relatives, feeding on the fruits or stems of cactus.

——WHERE THE DESERT TORTOISE LIVES. Tourists driving across the Mojave Desert in California are sometimes astonished to see fair-sized chelonians plodding across the road. Those more accustomed to seeing turtles basking on logs or on the banks of streams in the humid regions east of the Rocky Mountains, find it difficult to believe that such animals inhabit arid regions, sometimes miles from water.

A TORTOISE OF THE DESERT

A vegetarian like most of its land-dwelling cousins, the desert tortoise feeds on desert plants during the spring and summer rains. During dry spells it holes up in a burrow and lies torpid, or it sometimes lives on cactus.

None the less, dry regions, often with sparse vegetation, are the only parts of the United States where the desert tortoise lives. Those sent to zoological gardens in humid parts of the United States usually do not thrive. This tortoise shuns the denser vegetation of the chaparral along the coast of southern California, but captives sometimes live for years in such coastal cities as Los Angeles and San Diego. Occasional individuals have been known to breed in these metropolitan areas.

At the northern border of their range in south-western Utah, desert tortoises assemble in some numbers to hibernate in communal dens. Farther south, in Nevada and California, such dens have never been discovered, although winter burrows occupied by single individuals are common enough in some areas. We have no reports of tortoise burrows in the Colorado Desert of Arizona southward to the Río Mayo of Sonora in Mexico, although desert tortoises have been found in a number of localities.

Thus, in a single species we have a north-south trend in habits, which may be modified to fit local conditions. Winters are cold in Utah and the creatures probably could not survive without a deep retreat.

In the warmer regions to the south the desert tortoise needs only to cover its body by squeezing into a crevice or under vegetation to withstand the rigours of the milder winters.

——DESERT COURTSHIP. Desert tortoises have a strange courtship, the male approaching the female with neck extended and head bobbing. If the female withdraws her head and limbs, he nips clumsily at the edges of her shell. When competing males appear on the scene a fight usually ensues. Each male, with head withdrawn, faces his opponent, pushing with all his might. With shells engaged, one of the two may resort to a sudden twisting movement, overturning his opponent. The loser can right himself, but meanwhile the victor returns to his courting. More often the smaller of the two males flees, gaining astonishing speed for a tortoise.

The desert tortoise deposits two to six eggs in a hole dug in the sand, usually in June, two or three months after courtship. The eggs are white, an inch and one-half in diameter, and nearly spherical, with hard shells. The hatchlings, approximately an inch and a half long, begin to appear in the autumn. These are much less commonly found than the adults.

Berlandier's Tortoise, *Gopherus berlandieri.* Only two other tortoises live within the limits of the United States. One of these, much like its desert cousin, is Berlandier's tortoise. It dwells in rather a limited region, from central Texas southward into Nuevo León in

Mexico. During the warmer part of the year anyone making the trip through the arid region between San Antonio, Texas, and Monterrey in Mexico, is almost certain to see one or more individuals along the roadside.

Berlandier's tortoise tends to have a shell that is more dome-shaped than the flattened elongated one of its western relative. The habits of Berlandier's tortoise are much like those of the desert tortoise in Arizona, although relatively few observations have been reported. John K. Strecker came upon a female in Atascosa County, Texas, that was apparently having difficulties depositing her eggs in the rather hard ground. There were only three eggs, all of them oval in shape rather than spherical like those of the desert tortoise.

The Gopher Tortoise, *Gopherus polyphemus*. The third kind of tortoise inhabits the Gulf Coast, from eastern Texas to south-western South Carolina, and the drier, sandy areas of Florida. This tortoise is known to Floridians simply as "the gopher". In the Middle West and the West, the same name is applied to rodents, including the Pocket Gopher, which curiously enough is known in Florida as a "salamander"! Reputedly the use of this wrong name results from a corruption of the term "sand-mounder"—not an inappropriate one for the cheek-pouched rodent.

In any event, a "gopher burrow" in Florida refers to the hole dug by the tortoise. The creatures commonly dig them along well-drained sandy ridges or slopes, often in colonies. Usually they excavate the burrow to a depth of several feet, descending ten to more than twenty feet on a slope that varies from fifteen to thirty degrees to the surface.

The same burrow is occupied for years unless it is disturbed, in which case the occupant may move. The reptile comes out to feed upon the grasses and perhaps other succulent vegetation in the vicinity, but returns night after night to the same burrow. Most gopher tortoises are extremely shy. They are alert as they prepare to leave the burrow: the slightest movement in the vicinity will cause them to retreat. When an intruder comes upon a tortoise in the open, however, the gopher merely withdraws its limbs and its head, emitting a low hiss as it does so. Its head is protected by its fore limbs, which fit closely between the front edges of its shell.

The hind feet of the gopher tortoise are proportionately about half the size of those of the desert tortoise, in contrast to its head, which is relatively larger and more blunt. The gopher tortoise lays its eggs at the front of the burrow, in the pile of earth or sand accumulated during the excavation of its home. The eggs, like those of the desert tortoise, are spherical, and about seven-eighths of an inch in diameter.

The Painted Turtle, *Chrysemys picta.* No account of the common or interesting turtles would be complete without some mention of the painted turtle. This handsome chelonian dwells in the United States and southern Canada, from New England to beyond the Cascade Mountains of Oregon and Washington. There are four recognizable subspecies, one of which, *belli*, has invaded the Rio Grande drainage in New Mexico. It is unknown in several parts of the South-west, as well as in the peninsular portion of Florida.

THE ATTRACTIVE PAINTED TURTLE

The markings on the painted turtle give it an exceptionally handsome appearance. Its black, red, and yellow stripes and dots stand out effectively against the brownish or slate-coloured shell.

The habits of the painted turtle resemble, but are not, of course, identical with, those of the slider. The painted turtle is somewhat smaller—usually under seven inches long in the East, and a bit more than that in the West. It is definitely a water dweller and is commonly seen basking on logs or limbs overhanging pools or streams. But it is impossible to approach without causing it to scuttle into the water.

Observers have reported overland migrations, but these do not seem to be related to the breeding cycle.

Few turtles are quite so attractively marked. The large plates of the upper part of its shell are brownish or slate coloured, with yellowish edges. The marginal plates, however, are ornamented with red stripes or spots. The under-side of its shell is uniformly yellow in the eastern populations, except for the lower surfaces of the marginal plates. These are bright red, with black and yellowish markings. Its head is blackish, with two pairs of large yellow spots behind its eyes. Its throat is marked with yellow stripes that change to red farther back on its neck, and there are red stripes on its fore limbs and tail. Very young specimens have a yellow stripe down the centre of the shell. Individuals in the West often have yellowish instead of red markings, and the under-side of the shell is ornamented with a complicated pattern of black lines.

Other Common American Turtles. Other turtles that are relatively abundant in the eastern part of the United States must be mentioned. One of these, the Spotted Turtle, *Clemmys guttata*, is readily recognized by the yellow dots on a black ground colour. This is one of the smaller turtles, with a smooth shell length rarely exceeding four and one-half inches. It lives in ponds, ditches, and streams having a muddy bottom. Its range extends from south-western Maine, westward through a portion of Ontario in Canada to Michigan, and southward to northern Georgia. The spotted turtle is largely an insect-eater, although it also consumes worms, snails, slugs, and similar small animals, along with some vegetable matter.

Although related to the water-dwelling spotted turtle, the Wood Turtle, *Clemmys insculpta*, is approximately twice as long and spends much of its time on land. Its shell is rough, with each of the horny shields on the back raised as a sort of flat pyramid, the edges formed of concentric ridges and grooves. Wood turtles are not infrequently seen on highways in wooded areas in New England, where they feed largely on fruits, berries and herbs; but they do not spurn insects, snails, or other small animals. The species occurs as far south as the Virginias.

On the Pacific Coast another relative of the spotted turtle ranges from Baja California in Mexico to Oregon. This is the Pacific Pond Turtle, *Clemmys marmorata*, the only chelonian living in the fresh-

water streams of coastal California. Strangely enough, this rather
drab, olive or blackish turtle occasionally turns up on ocean beaches.
Although it is a water animal, the Pacific pond turtle is sometimes
encountered during its infrequent land migrations. In the water it
feeds on insects, but in the upper Sespe River of Ventura County,
California. I have watched it devour the plants growing on the bottom
of a clear pool.

THE SNAPPING TURTLES

Only two kinds of snapping turtles are now in existence, both of them
in the Americas. They belong to the family Chelydridae. Fossils found
in Europe indicate that snappers lived on that continent many millions
of years ago. Their nearest living relatives are the New World Mud
Turtles, *Kinosternon*, and Musk Turtles, *Sternotherus*, both genera of
which belong in a separate subfamily.

The Common Snapping Turtle, *Chelydra serpentina.* Few turtles
have quite the extensive range of the slider and its relatives. However,
the common snapping turtle is found throughout the streams and
ponds of most of eastern North America, from Canada to Mexico,
with relatives in Florida, Honduras and South America that should
doubtless be regarded as subspecies.

——THE FEROCIOUS SNAPPER. The snapper is a ferocious turtle.
When it is encountered on land it holds its ground, thrusting its head
forward and biting with such speed that the eye can scarcely follow
the movement. At such times its powerful jaws snap with a distinct
popping noise if they have not closed on the offender. On occasion
its large head may be launched with such force that its entire body
is carried off the ground.

Fortunately, perhaps, we rarely encounter snapping turtles on land.
In fact, I have seen them come out of the water of their own accord
only in Florida following a heavy spring rain. Normally they restrict
their activities to permanent bodies of water—ponds, lakes or sluggish
streams, usually those which have plenty of vegetation or a muddy
bottom.

Snappers have rather large heads and relatively long tails. The
under-side is poorly protected, the plastron being somewhat diamond-
shaped, rounded at the front, but tapering to a sharp point between

the hind legs. A narrow projection from each side connects it with the carapace, which is far more extensively developed. The limbs are stout and powerful, even though the snapper is rather a clumsy swimmer. It spends much of its time feeding on the bottom.

Karl Lagler analysed the stomach contents of 186 snappers taken in Michigan and found that about one-third of the food consisted of water vegetation. Another third was made up of insects, crayfish, clams, snails, and carrion. Game fishes made up the remaining third. He found little evidence for the widespread belief that they commonly seize game birds.

A FORMIDABLE TURTLE

The general run of turtles are conservative and inoffensive creatures, content to rely on the sturdy shells in which they are encased. Not so the snapping turtle; in biting, it thrusts its head forward with such lightning speed that its body is nearly lifted off the ground.

An adult snapper may weigh as much as twenty to thirty pounds, and there are occasional giants twice this size. The snapper is able to breed at a much smaller size, however, when the shell is no more than a foot long. The eggs are hard-shelled, somewhat smaller than a ping-pong ball, but quite as spherical and nearly as white when freshly laid. It may deposit as many as thirty eggs in a nest, the cavity of which may be almost any shape.

Owing to their water-dwelling existence, and more especially to their aggressive qualities of self-defence, snappers appear to have relatively few enemies except man. Although the meat is generally considered to be inferior, many snappers are sold as food, particularly in the markets of Philadelphia. Despite its ugly disposition, the snapping turtle's services as a scavenger probably more than offset its obnoxious habits.

The Alligator Snapping Turtle, *Macrochelys temmincki.* No other freshwater turtle in the United States attains the great size of the alligator snapping turtle. Individuals weighing 219 pounds have been reported. Specimens half this size are powerful enough to carry the weight of a man without exerting any noticeable effort.

The eggs of this great turtle are hard-shelled and spherical, nearly an inch and a half in diameter, and it lays them on the bank not far from the water. The hatchling is much like the adult except that it is covered with wartlike or smaller flattened protuberances. We know very little about its growth, although an alligator snapper that was well grown when received, lived for forty-seven years in the Philadelphia Zoological Garden.

Wickham tells of an alligator snapper thirty-four inches long and weighing fifty pounds that was liberated during July, 1918, in the Blue River of Oklahoma. A copper plate was attached to it in order to ensure future recognition. About two months later when the turtle was recaptured there was no appreciable change. The turtle was returned to the river, not to be seen again until July, 1921, when it was found eighteen miles upstream. What its travels may have been in the interim, it is difficult to say.

Captive individuals kept in ponds are not especially active. However, like all turtles, these ponderous reptiles must rise to the surface from time to time in order to breathe. The head, or only the snout, is thrust above the surface, air is exhaled and replaced with fresh air drawn into the lungs. Often the shell becomes covered with green algae, the long filaments of which completely obscure the animal as it lies on the bottom. Man appears to be the only known enemy of the alligator snapper. It is killed by fishermen, who resent its fish-eating

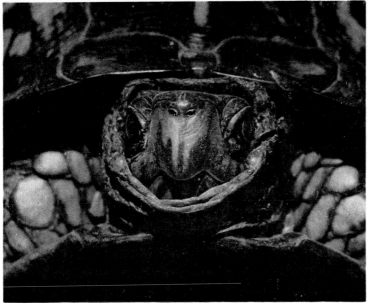

THE BOX TURTLE RETREATS BEHIND CLOSED DOORS

Turtles were in existence long before the dinosaurs. The secret of their survival lies in their tough, horny shells which have successfully provided them with shelter and protection. The protective element reaches its peak development in the box turtle's hinged plastron which can be shut tight against the domed carapace. Some individuals of this North American family get so fat on their diet of mushrooms, berries, snails, worms and caterpillars that complete closure of the shell is impossible and they are extremely vulnerable to attack. *See page 1253.*

THE FEROCIOUS SNAPPER IS DANGEROUS

Snapping turtles are the only aggressive species of this otherwise retiring, inoffensive group of reptiles. Like all members of the order, snappers are toothless, but the horny plates on their powerful jaws can inflict serious wounds. Turtle hatchlings in general have an "egg tooth" but they seldom use it; more often than not they rip a length-wise slit in the egg covering with the claws of their front or hind limbs. The females of many species may produce fertile eggs for three or four years after one mating. *See page 1272.*

SLEEK SEA GIANT

The close-fitting, comparatively flat shell of the green turtle is typical of the streamlined marine species that glide so efficiently through the ocean depths. The carapace is actually the turtle's modified, overgrown ribs, and the limbs are attached within the ribs. The skeletal structure of marine turtles is quite adequate as long as the animals remain in the water but on land it cannot support the great bulk attained by some species for any protracted period. Green turtles brought to market are usually placed on their backs to keep them alive as otherwise the skeleton collapses and they are crushed by their own weight. *See page 1278.*

Francis Christie

CUMBERSOME LAND GIANT

The size attained by all land-dwellers of the animal kingdom is limited by their skeletons and the 500-pound Galápagos tortoise is perfectly at ease where a marine species half its size would be in danger of its life if it came ashore. These giant tortoises are among the bulkiest of the still surviving land-dwelling reptiles but, like all too many other creatures, they are headed for extinction due to the carelessness and thoughtlessness of man. Hundreds upon hundreds have been slaughtered for food and oil, and the pigs (and probably also the dogs and rats) introduced by man into their island home dig up and devour their eggs. They do not breed in captivity, so the individuals in zoos in the United States and Europe offer no hope for the preservation of the species. *See page 1264.*

Allen J. Herman

habits. Many are captured alive and sent to market, although its flesh is considered to be only moderately palatable.

——How the Snapping Turtle Gets Its Food. This powerful brute lives in lagoons, swampy lakes, ponds or larger rivers in the Mississippi Valley as well as on the coastal plain from northern Florida to central Texas. The brown hues of its shell blend well with the muddy bottom where it lies motionless, angling for fish with a wormlike decoy that lies along the middle of its tongue.

While lying in wait, the turtle keeps its mouth wide open. The "worm", reddish in colour in contrast to the whitish lining of the mouth, is in constant motion. So closely does it resemble a squirming grub that it readily attracts fish. Before the fish can seize the bait, however, the huge jaws clamp down. It may eat other animals, but like the Surinam toad with its fish lure, the alligator snapper is obviously specialized as a fish-eater.

Naturalists described the angling device many years ago, although it was not until recently that anyone saw the turtle actually attract and seize its prey. However, at Silver Springs, in Florida, Mr. Ross Allen kept a few individuals alive in tanks where he could watch them feed. A few fish that escaped the jaws were rarely fooled a second time. The turtle caught fair numbers of each batch of fish placed in the tank, despite the wariness of some.

The alligator snapping turtle has no very close relatives that are still living, the common snapper being the nearest. The head of the alligator snapper is proportionately much larger—so large, in fact, that it cannot be completely withdrawn into the shell. Many observers have fancied that the great jaws were capable of severing a wrist or foot: it is commonly stated they will "cut off a length from a broom handle". But such nonsense is probably sheer supposition. Wilfred T. Neill thrust an ordinary lead pencil into the mouth of a fair-sized alligator snapper while we watched at Silver Springs. The pencil was broken but not severed, and it seems doubtful whether even the largest alligator snapper could bite through a broomstick.

The Snapper's Lesser Relatives. Mud Turtles, *Kinosternon*, with four species in the United States and many more in Latin America, are dull-brown creatures that turn up in virtually any sort of stream or pool in the lowlands, from the Atlantic Coast to the Colorado River in California. Like the Musk Turtles, *Sternotherus*, to which they are related, mud turtles sometimes emit an evil odour that makes them rather disagreeable to handle. Mud turtles can close their shell partially, each bottom lobe being hinged to the immovable bridge. This protective device is crude compared with that of the box turtle, which has a common hinge for the two lobes, so that one lobe swings on the other.

THE SOFT-SHELLED TURTLES

In the majority of turtles the body is protected by a bony shell covered with horny plates. The soft-shelled turtles have evolved in another direction. In most of this family, which has some two dozen members, bony shell has been reduced to a minimum. Their flattened bodies are covered with flexible, leathery shells. Apart from their peculiar body covering, they are readily identified by a long, flexible snout or proboscis.

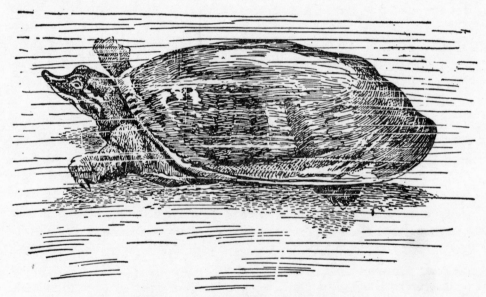

A TURTLE WITH A FLEXIBLE, LEATHERY SHELL

Circumstances alter cases for the Florida soft-shelled turtle, which flees from attack in the water but hurls itself boldly at its enemies on land. This turtle belongs to a group that differs from all living turtles in having a minimum of hard, bony shell.

The most ancient remains are from North America, where the family tree extends back well over a hundred million years. For several million years soft-shelled turtles (family Trionychidae) lived in Europe, where the family is no longer represented. The centre of distribution has now shifted to Asia and the East Indies, although there are several species in Africa. Some of the African turtles have flaps that cover the limbs when these are drawn in. This mechanism reminds us of the retractable landing gear on modern aircraft.

Three, or perhaps only two species, with several races—their relationships are not yet clear—inhabit the lakes, ponds, and rivers of the United States from the Colorado River eastward. These turtles are water dwellers, although the Florida Soft-shell, *Trionyx ferox*, occasionally migrates overland. In the water it is a powerful swimmer, retreating swiftly when molested. On land it makes no attempt to flee, but lurches toward the enemy with such speed that it nearly leaves the ground. This behaviour is doubtless the basis for the name *ferox*, Latin for "ferocious", an adjective likely to be applied to an animal that defends itself vigorously.

MARINE TURTLES

No account of the turtles would be complete without some mention of those that live in the sea. The half-dozen species recognized belong to two families. The Leatherback Turtle, *Dermochelys coriacea*, is the sole survivor of its group, the family Dermochelyidae. The other turtles living in the oceans are closely enough related to be included

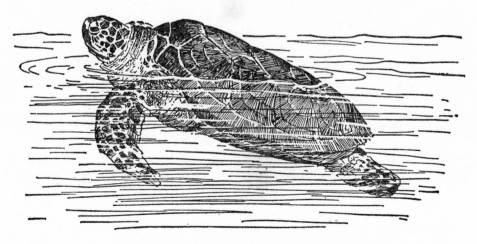

A TURTLE THAT APPEALS TO EPICURES
The tasty flesh of the green turtle gives turtle soup its delicious flavour. There is great variation in size among green turtles, ranging from 850-pounders to comparative midgets weighing about 200 pounds

in the other family, the Cheloniidae. For the most part these turtles are restricted to the warmer oceans. Occasionally they venture as far north as Nova Scotia or the English Channel, presumably carried along in part by the ocean currents.

The six sea-going turtles that visit the shores of the United States are rarely seen outside zoos or aquariums. However, from time to time, fishermen capture individuals of one species or another. Carcasses are occasionally washed up on the beaches. The Green Turtle, *Chelonia mydas*, the flesh of which is greatly esteemed as an ingredient of turtle soup, visits the shores of all continents. Individuals weighing 850 pounds have been reported, although those captured off the coasts of the United States commonly weigh less than two hundred pounds.

A TURTLE WITH A BEAK LIKE A HAWK'S
Valued as the source of tortoiseshell, the hawksbill turtle has a conspicuous beak that reminds us of a hawk. Occasionally we find a hawksbill with a shell a yard long and weighing as much as 160 pounds, but this is not large for a seagoing turtle.

The shell of the green turtle is covered with large shields that do not overlap. Usually it has only a single claw on each of its paddle-shaped limbs. As compared with the Loggerhead Turtle, *Caretta caretta*, and the Ridley, *Lepidochelys kempi*, in the Atlantic, and the Pacific Ridley, *Lepidochelys olivacea*, the head of the green turtle is relatively small. Commonly the loggerheads have two claws on each limb, although the smaller Ridley, *Lepidochelys kempi*, usually has three claws.

The Hawksbill Turtle, *Eretmochelys imbricata,* apart from the more pronounced beak that gives it its name, is readily recognized by the overlapping shingle-like arrangement of the thick plates on its back. These provide the so-called tortoiseshell of commerce for bracelets, combs, ornamental pins, and similar articles in Japan and Latin America. Celluloid has largely supplanted tortoiseshell in the manufacture of similar items in the United States. The hawksbill is not large for a marine turtle. Exceptional individuals may have a shell a yard long and weigh as much as 160 pounds.

The Leatherback Turtle, *Dermochelys coriacea,* is at the other extreme in size among the turtles that live in the sea. It is likely that this gigantic reptile is more than eight feet long. This was the measurement recorded for a specimen weighing 1,286 pounds; another, taken off Vancouver Island in the Pacific, weighed over three-quarters of a ton. It may well be that some leatherbacks weigh more than a ton, although this remains to be proved. In any event, among living reptiles only the largest crocodiles surpass the leatherback in bulk.

THE LEATHERBACK—A TURTLE COLOSSUS

This huge creature, some eight feet long, weighs well over half a ton. A powerful swimmer,
it has a hankering for deep water and comes ashore only to lay its eggs.

The leatherback, as the name implies, does not have the usual horny plates we find in the majority of turtles. The leathery skin, however, covers a bony shell that extends all the way from top to bottom, being made up of hundreds of little bony plates. These are somewhat irregular in shape, and fit together like a mosaic. The limbs, enormously developed as paddle-like flippers, have no claws. Seven prominent ridges extend down the back, presumably serving as stabilizers in lieu of fins.

Though leatherbacks are widely distributed and stray farther north than any other marine turtle, they are not abundant. One has been taken off Nova Scotia, and occasional specimens turn up in the English Channel. One captured off the coast of Ceylon had jellyfish in its stomach. The digestive tracts of others that have been examined contained seaweed, or marine algae. This powerful swimmer apparently prefers deep water and ventures on to shore only to lay its eggs. Several clutches each containing from ninety to 150 eggs, are laid each year. Other marine turtles have similar breeding habits.

THE SIDE-NECKED TURTLES

A side-necked turtle gets its name from the fact that it cannot withdraw its head into its shell. In its efforts to protect its head the turtle can do little more than bend its neck to one side of its shell, holding its head flush against the overhanging edges of the shell. Side-necked turtles (family Chelyidae) live only in South America, Australia and New Guinea, where some kinds are abundant. The one most commonly exhibited in zoological gardens is the South American matamatá.

The Matamatá, *Chelys fimbriata.* No living turtle is quite so outlandish in appearance as the matamatá, an inhabitant of the rivers of British Guiana and northern Brazil. In the not so distant past, large turtles, *Meiolania*, with goatlike horns, lived on some of the islands off the east coast of Australia. Unfortunately these passed into oblivion, leaving us with little knowledge of them beyond what we can glean from a few fossilized fragments of the skeleton. The matamatá has fared somewhat better, although it does not exist in great numbers. Its home territory is rather remote, but a few specimens are exhibited in zoological gardens.

The nose of the matamatá is a long soft tube with tiny nostrils at the tip. Its small eyes are placed very near the base of its prolonged snout. Its head and neck are as long as or even longer than the shell. Instead of withdrawing its head, the matamatá curls its long neck to one side under the margin of the carapace.

——How the Matamatá Takes Its Prey. The upper part of the shell is covered with lumpy yellow shields which remind us of those of the alligator snapper. But the matamatá has fringelike extensions of the skin of its thick neck, the sides and under-parts of the head. The extensions of the chin and throat, as well as the large ear flaps, are movable at will. The matamatá uses these appendages to attract fish.

A naturalist named Mahler kept some in an aquarium in Germany where he fed them regularly on live fish. He reports that the turtle assumes a lying-in-wait position in the water, following every movement of the prey. It turns its head cautiously and then holds it in one position. Waiting alertly, the matamatá sits motionless except for the movements of the queer appendages on its head. As the inquisitive fish come closer, the turtle's mouth suddenly gapes, its throat expands, and it draws the fish in with the onrushing water. Sometimes it engulfs two fish at the same time, usually head first. Mahler and other observers maintain that a loud sound accompanies the sudden movements of the jaws and neck.

The jaws of the matamatá are astonishingly weak and partly covered with a fleshy, liplike skin. Evidently, therefore, the mouth is not adapted for crushing or tearing the prey. On the other hand, the hyoid bones are greatly enlarged. These bones form the tongue attachment in mammals but in many reptiles they have been modified for special purposes. The whole muscular development attached to these bones is specialized to permit the sudden expansion of the neck. The matamatá, therefore, literally sucks its prey into the throat, along with the water. No other turtle is quite so peculiarly modified in this respect.

Despite such queer modifications in the matamatá, what we have read about the box turtle, slider, snapping turtles, marine turtles and others of this group reinforces the impression of exceptional inflexibility. The turtles present a remarkable contrast to the lizards, which are as versatile and adaptable as the turtle is conservative.

The Lizards

ALTHOUGH the role of the lizards is a relatively minor one in the present-day scheme of things, they are fascinating to study because of the endless variations that have arisen, so that each is equipped for its environment. We think of lizards basking in the sun; yet there are some that live underground, some that live in trees; some that glide in the air, some that swim—and some that run on the surface of water! The chameleon, with its colour-changing ability, its eyes that act independently of each other, and its tongue that darts some distance to snatch prey—this creature epitomizes the adaptability of the lizards.

Setting up definitions of the lizards and snakes entails difficulties. We therefore commonly place the two groups as suborders of the Squamata. (The lizards are in the suborder Sauria.) Some snakes have retained vestiges of hip bones and limbs, whereas some lizards have entirely dispensed with them. This makes it difficult to use such structures to distinguish between the two groups.

Even so, we might well consider each as a separate order, were it not for some of the odd "connecting links" that occur among both lizards and snakes. On the whole the evolution of the snakes has been quite separate from that of the lizards, from which they are descended. Each group has branched into several well-defined families. Despite the similarities between a few snakes and lizards, the snakes that one ordinarily sees are easily identified as snakes.

Lizards are descended from the same stock that also led to the dinosaurs, the crocodilians, and the birds. Their prominence in the fossil record began at about the time the dinosaurs were disappearing. Several different family groups, specialized in one way or another, arose from the original lizard stock. One family related to the Monitors, which include the largest lizard now living, invaded the ocean and preyed upon fish. This group of fish-eaters failed to survive for unknown reasons. Today there are no lizards inhabiting the oceans, although one large iguana enters it to feed on seaweed.

The common kinds of lizard are not vastly different in general appearance from the ancestral reptiles. Like the majority of mammals, including man, most lizards have four limbs, ten fingers and ten toes. But the legs and arms are attached farther out at the sides, so that a lizard can rest its belly on the ground without folding its feet under it as a cat sometimes does, or out to the side in the way that cows or horses do.

LIZARDS ARE REMARKABLY ADAPTABLE

There have been a great many changes in the feet and limbs of lizards to fit them for special ways of life. Those that live on the ground or climb in trees have extremely elongated toes, commonly with the fourth longer than the others. Many lizards, especially Geckos, have patches of greatly broadened scales under portions of the toes to form adhesive pads. These broad scales are bordered along the edges with tiny hairlike extensions that prevent the lizards from slipping when they climb on what appear to the naked eye to be smooth surfaces. Several kinds of lizards that habitually burrow in sand or humus have completely lost their limbs. Others are in intermediate stages, with the fingers and toes reduced in number; and in still others the limbs may be represented by what appear at first glance to be mere flaps of skin.

WHERE LIZARDS LIVE

Some lizards live on the surface of the ground, while others burrow under it. There are those like the large Tropical Iguana, *Iguana iguana*, that live in trees, or some like the American Anole, *Anolis carolinensis*, that dwell in shrubs as well. Still others like the Chuck-walla, *Sauromalus obesus*, prefer rocky places, where they seek shelter in crevices. Those called "Flying Dragons", *Draco*, have false ribs extending beyond the normal body outline. These are connected with thin skin to form "wings". The lizard does not actually fly but glides in somewhat the same manner as the flying squirrel or the flying fish, each of which really prolongs an initial leap. Such animals are gliders,

SCALY LIZARD OF THE DESERT

Guardian of the Joshua tree blossoms, the desert scaly lizard frequents the tree yuccas of the south-western deserts in the United States, preying upon the insects attracted to the creamy white flowers. This large lizard also lives in rocks, abandoned houses, and woodrat nests; it feeds on ants, beetles, small flowers, and sometimes smaller lizards.

rather than fliers, but in this limited way the lizards can be said to have invaded the air.

Similarly, no living lizard is truly a water-living animal, even though the Marine Iguana of the Galápagos Islands feeds almost exclusively upon the ocean plants known as marine algae. Others remain in the vicinity of water and do not hesitate to enter it. All lizards can swim after a fashion, and those that frequent stream banks or similar places are commonly excellent swimmers. Some of the larger Monitors, *Varanus*, have been seen swimming in the ocean some distance from land, which may account for their being found on oceanic islands. A small Cuban Lizard, *Deiroptyx*, spends much of its time in the water, and is a sort of counterfeit crocodilian. Its eyes are on the upper surface of its head so that the reptile is able to see even when the better part of the body and most of the head are submerged.

As you might gather from their several adaptations, lizards are a successful group. Today they are represented by nearly three thousand species. They are not quite so widely distributed as snakes, to which they gave rise, probably because most lizards are less tolerant of cold climates. In general, lizards are more abundant in desert regions and in the arid tropics, where they bask in the sun to raise their body temperature.

BURROWING LIZARDS

Not all lizards bask, however. Most members of one large family, the geckos, are active principally at night. Another family, the Amphisbaenidae (sometimes called "Worm Lizards" because many of them superficially resemble earthworms), is composed of burrowers that, with some exceptions, rarely venture to the surface. The eyes of these strange creatures are mere vestiges seen on some as black dots under the skin. Those that live in western Mexico and the southern end of the peninsula of Baja California have retained their front limbs. All other worm lizards have lost them completely.

THE "GLASS SNAKE"—NO SNAKE AT ALL

The so-called "glass snake" is actually a limbless lizard. It differs from snakes in a number of ways—its ability, for example, to grow a new tail if the original one is broken. There is no basis for the popular notion that this lizard can be broken in pieces and that the pieces will thereupon come together again.

These "worm lizards" are largely confined to the tropical and semi-tropical regions. Approximately fifty kinds live in Africa, and nearly as many are known in South America. In the United States there is only one species—confined to Florida. Some naturalists doubt whether these strange animals should be classified as lizards.

The "Blind Worm" of England and other parts of Europe, is neither blind nor actually a worm, being a limbless lizard, *Anguis fragilis* (which means "fragile worm"), with small but quite serviceable eyes. It might, like its American relative, the so-called "Glass Snake", *Ophisaurus ventralis*, be mistaken for a serpent. Both of these lizards retain traces of hip bones, indicating that their ancestors had limbs. They differ from snakes in having movable eyelids, in having the lower jaw bones that are solidly united in front, and in being able to grow new tails when this part of the body is broken off.

THE "GLASS SNAKE" MYTH

The common name "glass snake" is based on the mistaken belief that the body of the limbless lizard can be broken in pieces. Furthermore, if we are to believe a widespread myth, the pieces reunite. Sometimes called the "joint snake" for this reason, this reptile has a tail that when complete is considerably longer than its body. As with the majority of lizards, the tail readily becomes detached or broken if seized by an enemy. This enables the lizard to escape while the animal that intended to prey upon it is distracted by the squirming tail—for the tail may show some movement for several minutes after being severed from the lizard.

HOW LIZARDS GROW NEW TAILS

All lizards are able to grow a new tail when they lose this extension of the body. However, the new tail does not contain the vertebrae—bones that were a continuation of the backbone in the original tail. The one regrown is supported by a cartilaginous rod, the scales on the surface are commonly irregular and lack the definite arrangements seen on an unbroken tail. The new tail is rarely as long as the first one, and it generally lacks pigments in the skin that form some sort of pattern. The tail can be replaced any number of times, usually in a matter of weeks or months. When the tail is partly fractured, but not actually broken off, a tail will grow from the break, resulting in the tail's being forked. Ordinarily the plane of fracture is through one of the vertebrae, not between them, as one might expect.

HOW LIZARDS GET THEIR FOOD

The principal food of a good many lizards consists of insects, scorpions, centipedes, or other small creatures they see. The tongue has a muscular stalk that allows it to be thrust out suddenly, the fleshy end being covered with an adhesive saliva that adheres to the insect and pulls it into the lizard's mouth when its tongue is drawn back.

THE BASILISK—NO MYTHOLOGICAL MONSTER

In ancient lore, the basilisk brought instant death to anyone unfortunate enough to behold it. The real basilisk is harmless enough. This lizard runs across the surface of the water, moving its feet so rapidly that it goes some distance before breaking through the surface film. In Mexico it is often called the *paso-ríos* or "river-crosser". Basilisks also climb trees, but rarely venture away from streams or lakes. They patrol the banks in search of their insect prey.

Such lizards as the Gila Monster, *Heloderma*, the Skinks, and others having a forked tongue that can be thrust out, rely as much on their sense of smell as upon their sight to detect suitable food. It is interesting to note that only the groups of lizards with such tongues have given rise to true burrowers. We can ascribe this to the fact that lizards living underground cannot depend on vision and must rely upon their detection of odours that come from suitable food.

The forked tongue is thrust out repeatedly, and when it is withdrawn it carries odorous particles with it. Man, dogs, and similar animals detect odours by carrying them into the nose with the air they breathe. The endings of nerves that lead to the brain are located where the air passes over them. Lizards with forked tongues have similar nerves leading to the roof of the mouth, where the odorous particles carried in by the tongue come in contact with the nerve endings that pick up sensations and carry them to the brain. Thus what are sometimes called the "end organs" of smell are located in the roof of the mouth, but they are dependent upon the tongue.

TASTE AND SMELL

Taste and smell are closely associated, and taste appears to be better developed in some lizards than in others. Disagreeable food may be rejected, but many lizards will devour any small object resembling an insect if it is moving when seen. Millipedes, which produce an irritating substance on being disturbed, may be taken into the mouth and then hastily pushed out by the tongue or by violent movements of the head.

THE HEARING ABILITY OF LIZARDS

It has been shown that lizards are able to hear reasonably well, although few of them appear to pay much attention to sounds. When he was collecting the Giant Monitor or "Komodo Dragon", *Varanus komodoensis*, for the habitat group in New York's American Museum of Natural History, Mr. W. Douglas Burden set up a blind, like that used by duck hunters, where he could observe these huge lizards without being seen. He watched the cautious reptiles approach the dead pig that he was using for bait, thrusting out their long forked tongue as they came close enough to begin feeding. Whispering at first, Mr. Burden and his companions slowly raised their voices as they watched. The lizards were not disturbed, even when Mr. Burden tried shouting. Seemingly the great monitors paid not the slightest attention to sounds. Nonetheless, they fled when Mr. Burden emerged from his hiding place.

As a result of these observations, Mr. Burden was inclined to believe that the great monitors were possibly deaf, despite their rather well-developed ears.

Later, however, Miss Joan Proctor studied and noted the behaviour of one of these monitors kept in the London Zoological Gardens. After the animal became used to its surroundings, she found that it would respond to her call and come out from its place of seclusion to be fed, regardless of whether or not it could see her approach. Other more convincing evidence supports the belief that most, if not all, lizards can hear.

VISION IN LIZARDS

Some lizards that live above ground can probably see as well as many mammals. In the American tropics I have seen iguanas flee to safety when they apparently saw me coming toward them from distances of a hundred feet or more. Also experiments have now demonstrated that lizards, and probably all reptiles, can distinguish colours.

The eyes of many lizards have lids that can be closed when they are asleep, or when the eyes require protection. However, many geckos as well as the Night Lizards, *Xantusia*, lack movable eyelids, the eyes being covered with a transparent scale. Such lizards are mostly active at night, and nearly all of them have pupils like those of a cat, expanded and round in the dark, but contracted to mere slits when exposed to bright light.

Some skinks, the common Brown Skink, *Leiolopisma laterale*, of the eastern United States for example, have a transparent "window" in their lower eyelids.

THE IGUANAS

Iguanas are essentially New World lizards. The larger species are so bizarre in appearance that they are often exhibited in sideshows or in circuses as "Chinese dragons". Despite the fact that members of the family are absent from Old World continents, they are represented in Polynesia and Madagascar. As far as is known, all of them are daytime animals, active at night only when disturbed or routed from their sleep.

The lizards most commonly seen in the United States are likely to belong to the family Iguanidae, named after the lizard known throughout the American tropics as the "iguana". The common name, which is Spanish, but of Indian origin, serves also as the scientific name.

The Iguana, *Iguana iguana,* of the Americas, is the largest member of its family. In some parts of the tropics it occasionally attains a length, including the long tail, of over six feet. A row of greatly enlarged, hornlike scales down the centre of its back continues on to its tail. A large flap of skin, a dewlap suspended from its throat, has a fringe of small scales along its lower edge. On each side of its head, behind this dewlap and below the angle of its mouth, is a large, wartlike structure, conspicuous because of its lustrous-white, waxy appearance. Most of its head, including the dewlap, is bright green, with tinges of blue and brown. Its body, except for the row of spines, is covered with fairly small scales. It may be greenish or brown, with darker bars extending down on the sides.

——IGUANAS ARE AGILE. The sharp, powerful toenails of the iguana equip it for an existence in the larger trees of tropical lowlands. Young individuals are sometimes seen in shrubs, but like their parents they seldom stray far from water. The adults ascend to great heights in enormous trees, commonly selecting those with branches overhanging rivers. In the Jamastran Valley of Honduras I have counted as many as five large iguanas in a single tree.

Needless to say, it is not easy to capture these great lizards. When they are pursued by natives climbing the trees, or when wounded by rifle fire, iguanas will drop into the river below, where they swim with agility to the distant bank.

In the Yeguare River Valley of Honduras, I encountered one in the open along the edge of a small swamp that extended between two pastures cleared for cattle grazing. When I first saw the iguana it was basking on the bent trunk of a dead tree that had toppled. As I approached, the lizard abruptly dropped some eight feet to the ground and sped through the grass into a dense undergrowth of the swamp. It produced a loud swishing sound as it pushed its way through the dense vegetation. Apparently it didn't stop until it reached the centre of the swamp, for I could hear it over fifty yards away.

Occasionally my companion, Dr. A. F. Carr, and I saw iguanas on the ground along the banks of the river below this swamp; but more often we observed them in the branches of the gigantic fig and ceiba trees so characteristic of the American tropics.

——THE IGUANA AS A DELICACY. Throughout their vast range, from the tropical lowlands of Mexico to the Brazilian rain-forests, iguanas are considered an edible delicacy. Their flesh is white and

A marine turtle trudges resolutely across a Venezuelan sandbank in search of a suitable place to lay her eggs. Immediately the young hatch, they will head for the sea—and they never make a mistake in direction. Aquatic turtles would avoid many hazards if they could completely reverse the amphibian - to - reptile trend and lay their eggs in the water, but internal organ systems are singularly resistant to "backward" change. Other water-dwelling reptiles have made the "forward" adaptation and give birth to live young which can survive in their habitat, but the conservative turtle adheres to the ancestral pattern.
See page 1277

[11-1]

[11-1A]

It has been suggested that the American Indian name "terrapin" be restricted to the hard-shelled, freshwater species which are edible and have a recognized market value. The diamond-back, however, prefers the brackish water of the eastern, southern and Gulf coast salt marshes of the United States. Its market value as an epicurean delight almost led to its extinction. The high prices brought by the larger specimens have encouraged commercial "farming"; thus the salt-water terrapin is enjoying a respite.
See page 1959

The haunts of the yellow-bellied terrapin parallel those of the diamond-back, but at the western end of its range this chelonian gradually merges with its close relative, the slider. The slider family (named for the way they slide into the water at the approach of an intruder) is the most abundant in numbers, if not in species, in the United States. They are also equally at home in Mexico and Central America. *See page 1263*

[11-2]

[11-2A]

The Galápagos Islands off the coast of Ecuador were named after the giant tortoises which inhabit them, although the Spanish word "galápago" refers actually to a freshwater turtle and the bulky giants are strictly land-dwellers. How these tortoises got to the Pacific Islands is somewhat of a mystery, but as they can float and survive for long periods in sea water if they have to, naturalists think they may have been carried there accidentally from the South American mainland on floating driftwood. While they differ somewhat from island to island, the Galápago tortoises all belong to one species, With a life expectancy of 100 years, many of these giant tortoises complete their growth (ranging up to 500 pounds) before they are 20 years old. *See page 1264*

tender, not unlike that of frog's legs, and quite as tasty. In Honduras the natives prefer to roast or to bake females containing eggs. They leave the eggs inside and eat them with the flesh.

A LIZARD WITH A BODY TEMPERATURE OF 110° FAHRENHEIT

An inhabitant of the hottest, driest deserts in the United States and Mexico, the crested lizard or desert iguana is often abroad with a body temperature of 110° F. Sharing the habitat of the sidewinder or horned rattlesnake, this lizard sometimes succumbs to its deadly neighbour. Though the iguana can readily outdistance the rattlesnake, it is unable to escape the sudden thrust of the sidewinder's fangs if it comes within striking distance.

——How the Iguana Breeds. We know very little about the breeding habits of iguanas, although as many as eighty eggs are sometimes found in a single female. Presumably they lay the eggs in holes dug in the ground, probably with the coming of the rainy season. There is no real summer or winter in tropical regions. Annual breeding cycles are therefore usually keyed to the rainy season, which varies from region to region. But at some time of the year, probably depending upon the onset of the rainy season in each locale, young iguanas appear in great numbers as the eggs hatch. They are almost solid green in colour and much less gaudy than the adults.

These juveniles may occasionally eat insects, but the adults confine themselves to a diet of leaves, buds, fruits, and flowers. Both upper and lower jaws are provided with numerous close-set, sharp-edged teeth. These enable iguanas to snip off the vegetation with the efficiency of a pair of stout scissors.

The Marine Iguana, *Amblyrhynchus cristatus.* As the tropical iguana is such an efficient swimmer, it is not so astonishing that a close relative has managed to invade the margin of the ocean. On the isolated, rather barren Galápagos Islands off the west coast of South America, there are two large iguanas. One, a bulky, heavy-bodied, yard-long creature, perhaps heavier than the six-foot iguana of the mainland, lives on land. Despite the sparsity of the vegetation, it feeds on cactus flowers and fruits and other plants. This is the Galápagos Land Iguana, *Conolophus subcristatus.* The other is a slightly less bulky creature, of more or less the same proportions as its mainland relative. This is the marine iguana. It lives only along the coast of the islands, swimming offshore to feed on the marine algae or seaweed that grows on the rocky ocean bottom.

This marine iguana does not seem to have had any important

THE MARINE IGUANA—A SEAGOING LIZARD

About a yard long and quite bulky, the marine iguana lives along the coast of the Galápagos Islands. It feeds offshore, mostly on seaweed and other plants in the ocean.

enemies on land until the coming of man and introduced animals. In the sea it possibly falls prey to sharks or other large fishes. At any rate, when the great naturalist Charles Darwin visited the Galápagos Islands in the early part of the nineteenth century, he found that these sea-going lizards were seeking safety on land. They were present in enormous numbers along the rocky beaches, and Darwin readily approached them and picked them up. Those he tossed into the ocean immediately returned to land. The same individual repeatedly sought the shore when it could easily have escaped from Darwin by swimming away to sea.

It would appear to be a far cry from these large iguanas of the tropical regions to the common Fence Lizards, *Sceloporus*, the American Anole, *Anolis*, or the so-called "Horned Toads", *Phrynosoma*, of the United States. None the less these relatively small lizards all belong in the same family as the giant tropical iguanas.

The American Anole, *Anolis carolinensis*. The American anole is often known and sold at circuses as a "chameleon". The name derives from the anole's ability to change colour, from green to brown or the reverse, with some intermediate colours. Actually it is not even closely related to the true chameleons of the Old World, some of which are capable of much more extensive colour changes.

——THE ANOLE'S THROAT FAN. Sometimes anoles extend a throat fan. This ornament is not readily visible unless extended. A slender bone in its throat is attached at the front under its chin in such a way that it can be thrust forward by the attached muscles. This carries the skin with it, causing a fanlike extension of the throat, and exposing the skin, which is pink or red. Because of this throat fan, relatives of the American anole in Honduras are called "*pichete de bandera*" in Honduran Spanish. Translated this means "flag lizard", not an inappropriate name.

——RIVALRY AMONG THE MALE ANOLES. In their natural habitat each large male usually patrols a single area, frequently a single shrub or portion of a tree. Females or the young of either sex may enter this territory, but fully grown male intruders are kept out. Should they approach the male in possession, he extends his throat fan and arches his back, in somewhat the same fashion as a cat does when a dog comes near it. Usually the intruder flees; if he does not, a fight may ensue. The lizards bite each other, sometimes falling from the branch where the combat began. Ordinarily the resident male is the victor, and the intruder flees.

——How the Anole Changes Its Colour. The anole is an inhabitant of trees or shrubs in the humid portions of the south-eastern United States. When first seen it may be either green or brown, depending upon whether it has been in the shade or in direct sunlight. Ordinarily it is pale green when its body is quite warm, or when the animal has been in the dark. When exposed to bright light, or when its body temperature is low, it is usually brown. It may or may not match the colour of its surroundings. Green lizards will be found on brown branches, or a brown lizard may be sitting on a green leaf.

What brings these colour changes about is the movement of black pigment in some of the cells of its skin. When these cells expand they partly cover other cells and produce the brown coloration. But when the black cells contract to tiny dots that can be seen only by using a microscope, light is reflected from the other cells. The animal is then green. A tiny gland at the base of the brain produces a hormone that is carried in the blood. This substance controls the movements of the black cells. If the gland is removed—and this can be done by means of a rather difficult operation—the animal remains pale green. It is no longer able to expand the black pigment cells and turn brown.

——The Anole as a Pet. With proper care, the American anole can be kept as a pet. However, if it is to remain healthy for any length of time, it must be kept at a temperature of about 85° Fahrenheit, or a little lower. It needs moisture, which it likes to lap up from the leaves of plants. Hence these should be provided. In its native surroundings the anole probably relies for water upon the dew that settles on leaves during the night. A glass aquarium with a pane of glass over the top makes a good cage. The glass cover will make it possible to keep the air moist if some water is sprinkled in the cage every day. Lizards use so little oxygen that it should not be necessary to remove the cover more than once a day.

When the anole is in the glass cage it is possible to observe some of the interesting habits of this "false chameleon". It will eat insects but these must be alive and moving or the lizard will not find them. In addition to claws, the anole has adhesive plates under its toes. These enable the lizards to crawl or climb over smooth surfaces, even the glass sides of its cage.

Horned Lizards, *Phrynosoma*. The horned lizards, or "horned toads" as they are commonly called, are distantly related to the anoles, which belong to a separate branch of the iguana family. Most other members live in trees or shrubs, or at least climb them occasionally. But horned lizards live entirely on the ground, where their flattened bodies blend with their surroundings and make them extraordinarily difficult to see.

———How Horned Lizards Are Protected by Their Colour. Horned lizards found on red soil tend to be reddish, or when found on grey soil they are quite grey. There is always some sort of pattern consisting of blotches in pairs down the centre of the back. This pattern may hardly be noticeable if the lizard is found on fine-grained sand. Or it may be very distinct if the lizard lives in regions where the ground is strewn with pebbles. In other words, no matter where these lizards live they tend to have the kind of pattern that renders them least noticeable—the one that makes it most difficult for their enemies to find them. Moreover, the body of the horned lizard is so constructed that it casts no telltale shadow when the reptile is sitting.

———Where Horned Lizards Are Found. There are a dozen different kinds of horned lizards. One or more of these is found throughout most of the United States from Kansas and Nebraska westward to the Pacific Coast. They also range from Canada southward to the western side of the Isthmus of Tehuantepec in Mexico, the habitat of the largest of them all. They live in deserts, in prairies, plateaux, and mountains. I have found one kind at elevations of 10,500 feet in the San Francisco Mountains of Arizona, and another below sea level in the dunes near Salton Sea in California.

———Horned Lizards Live Mostly on Ants. Wherever the horned lizards live their food consists almost entirely of ants. Occasionally they devour small beetles or other small insects. A captive specimen of mine once ate a small garter snake. But they definitely prefer ants under normal conditions, although in captivity they will not always eat them. Some of the larger kinds have been observed sitting in front of beehives, devouring the bees as they come out.

Horned "toads" are not related to true toads, *Bufo*, which, of course, are amphibians. But they do resemble true toads somewhat in their manner of feeding. When an ant crawls close enough to attract the horned lizard's attention, the reptile moves up swiftly and then pauses, its eyes following every movement of the insect. Suddenly the lizard extends its tongue and snaps it back immediately with the insect adhering to its sticky tip. The whole movement is so swift that the insect appears to vanish abruptly, even though swallowing movements of the lizard clearly indicate what has happened. The lizard picks up larger insects in its jaws and sometimes rubs them violently on the sand before it takes them into its mouth.

——THE HORNED LIZARD'S SCALY SKIN. The skin of the horned lizard is mostly covered with small scales, with larger ones projecting at intervals. Often there is a fringe of enlarged scales or spines around the edge of its flattened body. There are also enlarged scales along the edge of its lower jaw as well. However, it is the scale-covered, horn-like structures which adorn the back of its head that give it the name "horned lizard". These "horns" are more pronounced in some species than in others. In general they are longer in the kinds of lizards that live in desert regions, and shorter in those of the plateaux, mountains, and prairies.

Apart from obscuring the body outline, thus making the animal more difficult to see, these horns and enlarged scales also serve as weapons of defence. Snakes are loath to attack horned lizards, although some of them do. But even while being eaten the horned lizard is sometimes able to retaliate. By twisting its head from side to side as it is being swallowed, it occasionally manages to puncture the neck of its captor. Dead snakes have been found with the lizard's horns projecting from the neck. Obviously the lizard has not saved its own life, but other members of its kind may be saved as the same snake can never prey upon them!

——BLOOD SQUIRTING. Horned lizards have another peculiarity that I first observed when, as an eight-year-old boy, I found a horned toad in Colorado and placed it on my white shirt. Looking down a few minutes later, I was startled to see a rather sizable blotch of blood on my shirt. Noting that one of the lizard's eyes was bloody, I suspected that the "toad" had squirted blood on me. Later I observed this peculiar behaviour in many other kinds of horned lizards.

However, only exceptional individuals spurt blood, usually immediately after capture. It is unusual for the captive to repeat the performance later on, as happened in the following case. In the company of an old Zapotec Indian, who was helping me collect specimens, I found one of the Giant Horned Toads, *Phrynosoma asio*, near the Mexican city of Tehuantepec. Shortly after I picked it up I saw a fine jet of blood come out of one eye. My Indian companion told me that in Spanish it was called "the lizard that cries blood", apparently in the belief that the bloody "tears" resulted from the lizard's weeping because it had been captured!

THE GIANT HORNED TOAD IS A LIZARD

The horned lizard is commonly (and confusingly) known as the "giant horned toad". It lives on the ground, not in trees, and it benefits from protective coloration. The scaly "horns" at the back of its head generally discourage snakes from attacking it.

Later I showed this same horned lizard to Mexicans farther north. They had never seen such a large one, and always marvelled at its size. To add to their interest, the poor lizard squirted blood from one eye virtually every time I took it from the bag to exhibit it. When I finally reached Palm Springs in California and showed the specimen to my brother, the lizard sent a jet of blood from each eye, some of the blood landing fully eight feet away.

——How the Horned Lizard Breeds. Most horned lizards that live at lower elevations lay eggs, but the kind that dwells on the plateau of Arizona retains its eggs within its body until they are ready to hatch. Near the town of Flagstaff, I caught a very large female one summer and mailed her to Dr. L. M. Klauber, the Curator of Reptiles in the

San Diego Zoological Garden. He sent me word later that the lizard had given birth to twenty-eight young while it was en route!

Horned lizards that lay eggs dig a hole in the ground where they deposit the eggs, usually in June. The eggs of most species in the United States hatch about seventy to ninety days later, when young horned lizards suddenly become abundant.

Stories of horned lizards being able to live for two or three decades sealed in cornerstones or similar places have no scientific basis. One animal that I accidentally left in a box in a cool basement storeroom was still alive a little more than a year later, but it was so emaciated that I could not save it.

The Scaly Lizards, *Sceloporus.* At one time members of the iguana family lived in many parts of the world. Today they are found outside the Americas only in the Solomon Islands and in Madagascar. But from Canada to Argentina they are the lizards most generally seen. The scaly lizards, the common kinds of which are often called "Fence Lizards", are extremely widespread. One kind or another is found from coast to coast in North America, and from New York to Panama.

THE FENCE LIZARD—AND ITS REPUTATION

Fence lizards have shingle-like scales that overlap. Most male fence lizards have blue patches on the belly or throat. The belief that "blue-bellied lizards are poisonous" is sheer fable. These active little creatures are found in most parts of the United States.

Fence lizards and their kin have rather large scales that overlap like shingles on a roof. However, there is a keel in or near the middle of each scale that extends beyond it as a small spine. Very few of these lizards are brightly coloured on top, but the males very commonly have large patches of blue on each side of the belly and sometimes on the throat. The statement that "blue-bellied lizards are poisonous", frequently heard wherever such lizards are found, is little more than a fanciful myth.

Other Relatives of the Iguana. The iguana family has many other interesting members. There is the Chuckwalla, *Sauromalus obesus*, for instance, a rather heavy-bodied lizard rarely as much as a foot and one-half long, which lives in rocky locations in the south-western deserts. For protection it crawls into crevices. If molested, it inflates its lungs, expanding the loose skin on its body against the walls of the crevice, thereby making it impossible for most enemies to remove it.

THE CHUCKWALLA MAKES A VIRTUE OF OBESITY

A rather plump lizard, the chuckwalla is named *obesus*. Its favourite haunts are rocky parts of the American South-west, where it can crawl into a crevice at the approach of danger. By inflating its lungs, it expands to crowd against the walls of its refuge; few enemies can pry it loose.

There are four kinds of Fringe-footed Sand Lizards, *Uma notata* and its relatives, in the United States and Mexico, all of them living in desert regions where wind-blown sand forms dunes. Scales extend along each toe forming a sort of fringe that apparently helps these lizards to run more efficiently over loose sand. The fringed toes are used in much the same way that man uses snowshoes to walk on loose snow. These lizards frequently bury themselves in the sand, and sometimes "swim" for short distances beneath the surface. They have spade-shaped noses, with the lower jaw fitting so snugly into the upper that sand does not penetrate the mouth. The special structure of the nostrils prevents sand from getting into the lungs when these lizards are below the surface.

The Basilisks, *Basiliscus vittatus* and its relatives, are quite as bizarre as any lizard in the Americas. The name is from the Greek word, Basiliskos, meaning a kind of serpent, and was first applied to a creature famous in European mythology. The mythological basilisk, quite unlike the real ones, was a dragon so terrible that its gaze or breath invariably proved fatal to those who had the ill fortune to encounter it.

Basilisks, with their long tails, may exceed two feet in length, but they are quite harmless despite their strange appearance. Fully grown males have a thin extension of the skin at the back of the head that is pliable but stiffly supported. This gives the lizard a windswept appearance. The head of this creature looks more like an old-fashioned automobile radiator cap ornament than something belonging to a living animal.

Wherever basilisks are found in Latin America, their textbook name is replaced by such names as *"paso-ríos"* or "river-crossers" in allusion to the reptile's ability to run across the surface of water. In other places they are called *"Jesús Cristo"* lizards for the same reason. Apparently the lizard's ability to travel on water is largely a matter of its moving its feet so rapidly that the water provides enough resistance to support the weight of its relatively light body. If the lizard slows down or pauses, it sinks to the surface of the water and continues on its way by swimming. It does not use its front legs for rapid running, whether on land or water. Not unlike some of the extinct dinosaurs, basilisks and several other lizards, notably Collared Lizards, *Crotaphytus collaris*, run on their hind legs, with the front of the body raised well off the ground and their fore limbs pressed to the sides.

THE BEADED LIZARDS

The only lizards known to have acquired grooved teeth and a specialized saliva or venom, are the beaded lizards (family Helodermatidae).

There are only two species, both of them in western North America. The species dwelling in the United States is discussed below. The Mexican species, known to natives as the "*escorpión*", is the larger of

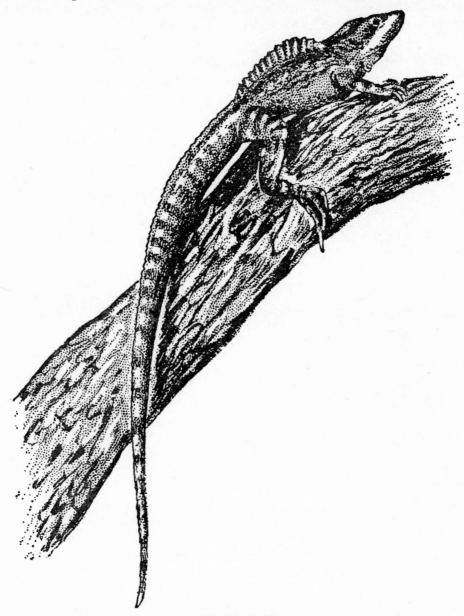

MALE BASILISK

Only the fully grown male basilisk has the high crest on its back. Young basilisks, whether male or female, look pretty much like their mother, but only the male grows up to look like his father. Females not only lack the crest, but never reach the size of the male.

the two. It lives along the Pacific Coast in the Mexican states that
extend from Sonora to Chiapas. A lizard, *Lanthanotus*, that lives in
Borneo, was said to be related to the beaded lizards, but this has not
proved to be so. The Bornean species is not venomous, and turns out to
be more closely related to the monitors.

The Gila Monster, *Heloderma suspectum* (Spanish, pronounced
"Hee-la"), is the only venomous lizard found in the United States. It
gets its name from the fact that white men first came to know this
potentially dangerous reptile in the valley of the Gila River of Arizona.

THE GILA MONSTER—REALLY VENOMOUS

Some lizards with a reputation for being able to inject venom are really harmless. The
Gila monster, which dwells in the deserts of the American South-west, has the reputation,
and the venom too! However, this "monster" (less than two feet long) bites only on
provocation. Its venom, drop for drop, is as potent as that of some rattlesnakes.

The Gila monster is confined to the desert regions of the South-west,
principally Arizona and the adjacent states except California, but
including the Mexican state of Sonora. It is a rather large lizard,
though rarely as much as two feet in total length. Despite its blunt nose,
beady black eyes, and stocky build, it is not entirely unattractive-
looking. Its skin, filled with tiny round bones that give it the beaded
appearance, is brightly marked with black bars or cross-bands on a
whitish yellow or pink background.

——THE GILA MONSTER'S VENOM. The Gila monster moves slowly,

but if it is molested it turns and snaps with the speed and ferocity of an angry tomcat seized by the tail. Few people are bitten, however, except those foolish enough to handle captive specimens carelessly. But when the Gila monster does bite, its jaws clamp down with un-believable force. Relaxing a little and then applying its powerful muscles, it forces its grooved teeth deep into the flesh of its victim. Venom from glands in the lower jaw flows into its mouth and slowly seeps into the grooves of the teeth. Meanwhile the lizard hangs on with all the force it can muster.

Crude as this mechanism is, it does manage to get its venom into the victim. This lizard lives largely upon the eggs of birds that nest on the ground. Upon rare occasions it devours small rabbits or lizards. It is doubtful, however, whether the venom is used as a means of killing such prey. Snakes use their fangs to subdue the animals they intend to eat—the use of their fangs in self-defence is quite incidental. In direct contrast, the Gila monster's venom apparatus serves largely as a protective device, quite unnecessary in the animal's food-getting activities.

THE DRAGON-LIZARDS OR AGAMIDS

The members of the family Agamidae rather resemble the iguanas, from which they may be distinguished by their teeth. In iguanas the teeth are attached to the inner side of the jaw, in contrast to the dragon-lizards, whose teeth are set in sockets on the ridge of each jaw. The Agamidae are widely distributed in the Eastern Hemisphere, including Africa and Australia. The domains of the two families do not overlap, for dragon-lizards are not represented in the Americas, in Madagascar, or in the Polynesian Islands inhabited by iguanids. The dragon-lizards have crests, dewlaps, and other ornamental appendages resembling those found on iguanids. Like the latter, they are essentially daytime creatures in their activities.

The Flying Dragon, *Draco volans.* The Flying Lizards are the only living reptiles that have made any great success in the air. One group of ancient reptiles, the pterosaurs, took to the air on wings and actually flew. Their wings were somewhat batlike, except that the skin forming the wing surface was supported by the arm and a single greatly elongated finger—the fourth. The pterosaurs disappeared millions of years ago. Meanwhile another group of reptiles had passed through the successive stages that led to the warm-blooded birds, an eminently successful group that now outnumbers the reptiles.

Thus the ancient pterosaurs and the birds perfected their powers of flight. Each in its own way managed to propel itself while in the air.

——THE LIZARD THAT "FLIES". The present-day reptiles in their methods of flight are more like the "flying" fish, which launches itself from the water and sails or glides above the water. The so-called "Flying" Snake, *Chrysopelea*, of Asia merely flattens its body and launches it outward from a tree trunk in a relatively steep glide. *Draco volans*, despite its name, which means "flying dragon", is actually only a glider, too, but a far more efficient one than the flying snake.

The flying dragon is but one of more than three dozen related species that have acquired the "wings" necessary for volplaning from tree to tree. These wings consist of a thin membrane of skin supported by some half-dozen false ribs that extend beyond the normal outline of the body. When this slender lizard rests or climbs about on trees in search of food, these expansions of the skin and ribs can be folded back along the sides of its body. The flying dragon ordinarily pauses with its head uppermost on the trunk of a tree, and at that time it is nearly invisible because its colour blends with the bark. But, owing to the bright colours beneath the wings, it has been described as resembling a flashing blue gem as it darts through the air overhead.

All flying lizards are gaudy, colourful creatures when their wings or parachutes are spread. Furthermore, their bizarre appearance is heightened by a long pouch suspended from the throat, as well as by a flap or wattle on each side of the head. The throat pouch, like that of the American Anole, *Anolis*, can be distended or thrust forward, sometimes beyond the front of the head. The wattles too are erectile and can be raised by the male during courtship.

——WHERE THE FLYING LIZARD LIVES. These lizards are especially abundant in coconut and betel palm plantations. They are nimble and active, moving about in a jumpy fashion on the tree trunks where they habitually feed. They are virtually never seen on the ground, although they apparently descend to lay their eggs. Ordinarily after it has searched one tree and devoured all the small spiders, or insects including ants, moths, flies, and even grasshoppers, the flying dragon suddenly launches itself into the air.

——How the Flying Lizard "Flies". The flying lizard is said to direct its flight with precision, sometimes gliding through the air for a distance of sixty feet before it settles on the trunk of the tree it has chosen as a landing place. The lizard spreads its wings only after it has taken off. It lives almost continuously in the highest treetops, descending somewhat at the end of each glide. Its flight is at a slight angle downward from the horizontal, however, and it tilts sharply upward when it alights. It always lands with its head upward. It prefers vertical trunks as landing fields.

——Courtship and Breeding Among the Flying Lizards. Male and female meet each other with their wattles and throat pouch distended. Dr. Karl P. Schmidt watched the Celebes Flying Lizard, *Draco spilopterus*, and saw the male spreading and folding its parachute, apparently as a courtship display. Dr. Malcolm Smith notes that these lizards are always seen in pairs, hunting in close company. He believes that having once paired, flying lizards remain together throughout the season.

Dr. Schmidt's observations of the Celebes flying lizard, mentioned above, are of such special interest that they merit quotation in greater detail.

"On these days [21 and 22 June] *Draco spilopterus* was abundant in the rather open hardwood forest which clothes the slopes of Lambeh. The longest glide observed was perhaps thirty feet, there being no occasion for longer flights. These lizards glide at a low angle and alight without shock after only a very slight upturn. Mr. Walter A. Weber, the expedition artist, and I were fortunate in witnessing what appeared to be the courtship display of these lizards. A female, with wings folded at her sides, clinging head upward on a tree trunk a dozen feet distant from our station and twenty feet from the ground, was approached from above by a male, who advanced to within a few inches of the female, halted, and went through bobbing motions like those of the American anole, familiar to American herpetologists. As the anterior part of the body was raised, the coloured dewlap was distended to its fullest extent, and at the same time the brilliantly coloured wings were extended to the greatest possible degree. In this posture the bobbing display was continued for perhaps a minute. At this juncture a second male flew from a tree near us to the tree on which the courtship was in progress, ran up the tree and engaged the first male in combat. This struggle was so violent that both animals fell from the tree. They disengaged in mid-air, and sailed off to separate trees. The recovery of balance in mid-air and the ability to direct the flight to a suitable landing place is an interesting testimony to the perfection of gliding flight attained by these lizards.

LIZARDS THAT "FLY"

Some lizards are equipped with a thin membrane supported by false ribs jutting out beyond the normal outline of the body. By spreading the membrane, these creatures can glide as much as sixty feet at a time. Flying lizards spend virtually all their life in trees.

"Whether the bobbing motions and display of the coloured wing and throat membranes are for the attraction and excitation of the females or solely for sex recognition, it seems clear that the brilliant coloration of the wings is correlated with this secondary use. There is even the interesting possibility that these unique structures originated as a secondary sex character, and that their use in gliding flight is secondary."

Felix Kopstein, whose studies of reptiles in Java are unsurpassed, found two eggs of the flying dragon in his garden during the latter part of July. These were nearly an inch long and covered with a

One of three species of tortoises found in the United States, the gopher tortoises inhabit the Gulf Coast from eastern Texas to south-western South Carolina, and the drier, sandy areas of Florida. They live in burrows dug from 10 to 20 feet into well-drained sandy ridges or slopes, and will occupy the same burrow for years unless molested. Like all tortoises ("land-dwelling chelonians") the gopher is a vegetarian.   See page 1269

[11-3]

The smooth-shelled spotted turtle lives in muddy-bottom ponds, ditches and streams from south-western Maine west to the Great Lakes and south to Georgia. One of the smaller turtles (three to five inches), it feeds mainly on insects although it also consumes worms, snails, slugs and some vegetable matter. It eats only when it is in the water.   See page 1271

[11-3A]

[11-3B]

The wood turtle belongs to the same family as the spotted turtle, but it has a rough shell, is twice as big, and spends most of its time on land. It will eat insects and snails, but it prefers berries, fruits and herbs. Wood turtles range from New England to Virginia. The Pacific Coast pond turtle is also a member of this group of semi-aquatic turtles. Six other species spread from southern Europe through Asia to Japan.   See page 1271

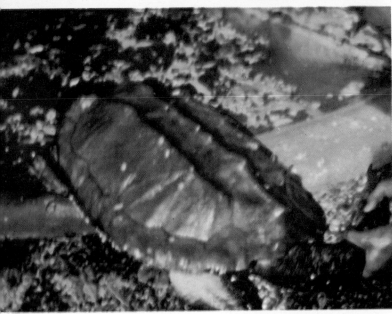

The only two surviving snapping turtles and their nearest living relatives, the mud and musk turtles, are exclusively New World species. The common snapper has the widest distribution. Ferocious turtles which may grow to 20 or 30 pounds, the common snappers seldom leave the water of their own accord, restricting their activities to permanent bodies of water with plenty of vegetation or a muddy bottom. They feed on the vegetation as well as game fish, snails, clams, crayfish and carrion.

See page 1272

The alligator snapping turtle is by far the largest freshwater turtle in the United States—individuals weighing up to 219 pounds have been reported. They are further distinguished from the common snapper by the three pronounced ridges on the coffee-coloured shell. Nature has endowed the alligator snapping turtle with a built-in fish lure—a wormlike reddish decoy that lies along the middle of its tongue. The turtle, well camouflaged on a muddy river bottom, lies in wait with its mouth wide open, dangling the "worm", but before a hapless fish can seize the bait, the big jaws snap shut on it. Alligator snappers frequent the lower Mississippi Valley and the Gulf Coast from Florida to Texas.

See page 1274

[11-4A]

[11-4B]

The mud turtles are familiar species in the United States and Latin America but do not range into South America as do the common snapping turtles. Like their nearer relatives, musk turtles, mud turtles sometimes emit a foul-smelling odour that makes them disagreeable to handle, Much smaller than the snappers, mud turtles have a comparatively more expansive plastron which is hinged somewhat like that of the box turtle, enabling them at least partially to close the shell.   See page 1275

THE CHAMELEON'S SNARE

Only the chameleon among all reptiles has a tongue that can be extended to a distance greater than the length of its body. The sticky mucus on the tip of the tongue catches on to insects, which are drawn into the mouth to be crushed by the teeth prior to being swallowed. See page 1310.

Pat Kirkpatrick—National Audubon Society

HIDER IN THE SANDS

Confronted by an enemy, this desert lizard will put up a courageous fight. If the danger is too great, however, the animal can quickly sink beneath the sand by vibrating its body.

Arabian American Oil Company

A DWELLER IN THE ARABIAN DESERT

This rock lizard (*Agama*) bears superficial resemblances to some not-so-close relatives inhabiting arid regions in the Americas. The specialized teeth so conspicuously present in the front of the mouth assist the lizard in grasping insect prey. *See page 1303.*

parchment-like shell. On 13 August, the young, two and one-half to three inches long, appeared. On 30 October of another year he observed a female lay five eggs that hatched on 28 November. Few reptile eggs hatch after so brief an interval unless development is already under way prior to their being laid. Whether the eggs of the flying dragon undergo prior development, remains to be found out.

No one has ascertained whether the flying lizard establishes territories and defends them against intruding males. Apparently there is some competition among males, however, for Dr. Smith quotes the statement of Mr. G. F. W. Elwes who saw two of them fighting. While Mr. Elwes watched the combat, one or the other occasionally lost its footing and fell. Its wings were quickly spread, however, and the lizard managed to glide back toward the tree to hunt up its adversary again and renew the fight. A third lizard, presumed to be the female, put its head around the trunk at intervals as though interested in seeing how the fight progressed.

Lizards of the Old World and the New. Flying lizards have a peculiar distribution. One species is found in southern India, but the others all live in the south-eastern extremity of Asia, from Assam to the East Indian Archipelago, and the Philippine Islands. No flying lizards have been seen between Central India and the Burmese border—a distance of about a thousand miles.

Some members of the Old World Agamidae family, as we have noted, have a certain amount of resemblance to the New World relatives of the iguanas. Thus, the American Basilisk, *Basiliscus*, has its counterpart in the crested, casque-headed lizard of the Philippines. The chuckwalla of the arid peninsula of Baja California is roughly similar in form and habits to the Spiny-tailed Lizards, *Uromastix*, of desert regions in Asia and Africa. In fact there are many striking parallels, some closer than others, between species in the separate families. Australia's Thorny Devil, *Moloch horridus*, is the counterpart of the American horned lizard.

No lizard in the New World bears even the slightest resemblance to the flying dragon and its close relatives. Some small tree-dwelling lizards, such as the Anoles, *Anolis*, do not fall in a direct line when dropped. The surfaces provided by their feet and bodies may cause them to veer away from the perpendicular to some extent, but this is scarcely gliding in the sense that the dragon performs its aerial manoeuvres. The pterosaurs, as we have seen, suffered some sort of evolutionary crack-up. But today the flying lizards are evidently successful—perhaps as much so as the flying fish, the flying squirrels, and the few other animals that use gliding as an efficient means of escaping from their enemies or moving from place to place to feed.

A LIZARD WITH A FORMIDABLE SPIKED TAIL

The spiny mastigure is an Arabian lizard that manages to support itself on vegetation in one of the most barren deserts of the Old World. In fact, it succeeds in attaining a greater size than any other member of the rock lizard family. Its spiny tail, rather like a spiked war club in appearance, is a formidable weapon.

The Frilled Lizard, *Chlamydosaurus kingi.* Frightening devices or "scare organs" have evolved in a number of reptiles, but none is quite so spectacular as the one employed by the frilled lizard. This agamid is an inhabitant of tropical forests in northern Australia and New Guinea, where it feeds on beetles and other insects that frequent the bark of trees. The most remarkable feature of the animal, however, is its large frill—a vast expansion of the skin on each side of the neck. These expansions join across the throat, where they are intimately connected with extensions of the hyoid bones in the throat. Specially modified muscles attached to these bones erect the frill at the same time that the mouth opens.

——THE FRILL AS A DEFENCE MECHANISM. Ordinarily, when the

lizard is foraging on the trunks or the lower limbs of trees, each side of the frill folds back neatly in four pleats on its neck and shoulders. Upon the approach of a threatening assailant, however, the frill is suddenly erected like an umbrella being opened. When at bay, a thirty-inch lizard expands a frill that is nearly ten inches across. The widely gaping mouth, red inside, adds to the animal's formidable appearance. In Australia dogs that have learned to pursue and kill other equally large lizards refuse to come to close quarters with the frilled lizard.

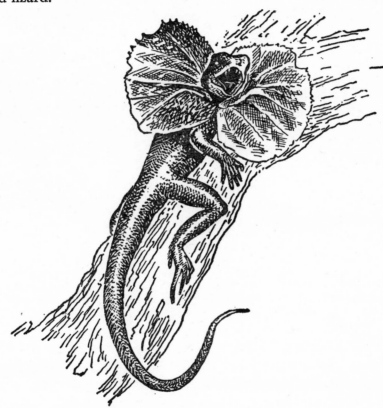

A FRILL WITH DEFENSIVE VALUE

A frill that is no "mere frill" is possessed by the lizard pictured above. This creature has a considerable amount of loose skin about its neck. When the frilled lizard opens its mouth, the skin is stretched taut, giving the animal a most frightening appearance.

When running, the frilled lizard uses all four limbs only at the start. As it gains momentum, the reptile raises its body to an erect position and runs on its hind legs. It covers forty or fifty feet at a stretch, coming to a stop sitting high on its haunches. After resting for a moment, the lizard resumes its running course. Aside from its ability to get about on two legs, and its method of frightening an enemy, the frilled lizard is remarkable in being almost equally at home on the ground or in a tree.

THE TRUE CHAMELEONS

No other family, as a whole, is quite so specialized in one direction as the chameleons. All members of the family possess an extraordinary tongue and amazing modifications of the toes that transform them into grasping mechanisms. None of the chameleons is adapted for rapid movement on land, although the species that lay eggs must descend to the earth to build their nests. Some give birth to fully formed young, quite possibly while clinging to the tree or shrub they live in; the process has never been observed under natural conditions. There is some evidence that the live-bearers give birth to their offspring individually, at delayed intervals, rather than in rapid succession.

The tail, like the feet, is a grasping organ, except in some smaller African species that have been referred to separate genera, *Rhampholeon* and *Brookesia*. Here the tail intensifies the resemblance to a leaf, the outstretched tail serving as the "stem" when the body is viewed in profile. The "casque head" is characteristic, but all sorts of projections from the head, including "horns", crests, prolonged snouts, have evolved in the various species. In the majority of them the body is under four or five inches in length. A few species are relatively huge, with bodies up to a foot long. If the prehensile tail is included, the total length approaches two feet. The chameleons make up the family Chamaeleontidae.

The Common Chameleon, *Chamaeleo chamaeleon*. The chameleon has been aptly characterized as the possessor of "the most amazing tongue in Nature". This grotesque reptile is specialized in so many respects, however, that it would be equally valid to single out any of its other remarkable qualities.

The chameleon's fingers and toes are split into opposing bundles, with three on the outer and two on the inner side in the feet, but with the reverse arrangement in the hands. Its eyes are housed in cone-shaped turrets, and each can be focused independently of the other. One eye may be directed upwards, while the other is trained toward the rear. When the creature is in search of food each eye is continually revolving in all directions. When the animal sights its prey, however, it focuses both eyes upon the object.

——THE CHAMELEON'S AMAZING TONGUE AND HOW IT WORKS. Most chameleons prey upon insects, grasshoppers in particular. So slow and deliberate are the chameleon's movements that it is doubtful whether the victim is aware of its approach. When the lizard is perhaps a foot away, it pauses, watching intently with both eyes as though taking aim. Its mouth opens slowly and the pink, clublike end of its tongue protrudes. Abruptly the insect vanishes from its resting place. It happens so quickly that an observer gets only a fleeting glimpse of the tongue as it shoots out to its full length. An instant later the grasshopper is being crunched between the chameleon's teeth as the lizard prepares to swallow its food.

This astonishing performance is made possible by the unique development of the mechanism that provides for the extension of the tongue. This is a tubular stalk for the club-shaped end with the sticky secretions that ensnare the prey. The tubular portion is drawn back over the tapering end of one of the hyoid bones in the throat. The stalk is made up of a series of circular muscles that can be contracted rapidly, one after the other. As they contract on the slippery end of the bone, the tube, which has been drawn back on the bone like a spring on a stick, is propelled forward. The principle involved is the same as that utilized to eject a fresh watermelon seed from the hand by squeezing it between the thumb and finger. Contraction of other muscles in the chameleon's tongue causes it to be rapidly withdrawn into the mouth, carrying the morsel of food on its adhesive tip.

——HOW THE CHAMELEON CHANGES THE COLOUR OF ITS SKIN. People think of the chameleon as being an animal that can change the colour of its skin to match any object upon which it is placed. Actually, this queer lizard is able to change its colour only from green through yellow to dark grey. Sometimes it may be halfway between any two of these colours. When it is in a dark room with no light whatsoever, it becomes yellow. When it is placed on a dark object in strong light it becomes dark grey. On the other hand, if it is placed on a light background in bright light it becomes yellow. Before you can understand how these changes are brought about, you must know something about the chameleon's skin.

If you look at a slice of this skin under a microscope you can see that, as an outside layer of the body, it is made up of little cells.

These cells look somewhat like a number of grapes of different colours in a layer of pale jello. However, the cells are very much smaller than grapes, so that we cannot see them unless they are greatly magnified by the microscope. Most of these very small cells near the top are yellow in colour. Some of the cells in between are black, while others on the bottom of the layer are whitish. These white cells, like mirrors, serve as reflectors. When the chameleon appears to us to be yellow it is because we see only a great number of larger yellow cells. A smaller number of tiny black cells are present, but we do not notice them unless the skin is examined under a microscope.

You will have some idea why the lizard seems to be green to us at the times when these black cells are not expanded or "blown up", if you remember what happens when you write with blue crayon on a piece of paper, and then write over the blue with yellow pencil. Yellow on top of blue looks green to us. This is almost the same thing that happens to the chameleon's skin. The white cells on the bottom of the layer of the chameleon's skin reflect blue light. When this blue light passes through the yellow cells it appears to us to be green light; in other words, the chameleon looks green.

Now what happens if the black cells, those in between the white layer on the bottom and the yellow layer of cells on the top, begin to expand?

The cells that appeared under the microscope as black dots now grow larger, with fringelike extensions in outline. They fill up the space between the white layer and the yellow layer. Like a black window shade in front of a mirror, they cut off all the blue light that the white cells on the bottom have reflected. As a result the top layer is almost all we see. The chameleon now appears to be a yellow lizard.

But suppose those same little black balloon-like cells, with fingers extending outward from them, continue to expand. They spread outward into the top layer, and begin to surround the yellow cells. Finally we can scarcely see the yellow cells at all. Nearly all we see is the black cells. Then the lizard looks as though it were dark grey or blackish.

——How the Chameleon's Nervous System Produces Colour Changes. What makes these black cells grow big or remain small? You have heard about nerves. You know that if you are stuck with a pin on the end of the finger a nerve carries a "message" to your central nervous system. You realize that you have been hurt. You jerk your finger away from the pin. While this is not what happens when the chameleon's colour changes, it will give you some notion of the way in which the nerves carry "messages" to other parts of the body.

In fact, we can think of nerves as electric wires, somewhat like those that lead to an electric light. When you press a button, the light goes on. The chameleon has tiny cells in its skin and eyes, and these cells serve the purpose of press-buttons. When light reflected from a dark object falls on these tiny cells in the eye the effect is much as though someone had pressed a button. Instead of a light turning on, however, the black cells begin to grow larger, like a balloon being inflated. Then, as we have explained above, the chameleon turns blackish in colour.

THE AMAZINGLY VERSATILE CHAMELEON

This small but adaptable lizard has a host of remarkable qualities. With its swivel eyes it can look in different directions at the same time. To get its food, it uses its long, sticky tongue to good advantage. It is able to grasp objects with its tail. Above all, it is famous for the way it changes colour, even though it does not always match its background.

Now suppose we put the chameleon in a dark place, so that no light reaches the little "press-buttons" in the skin, or in the eyes. It is as though the electric current had been turned off. The black cells again become small dots. What happens to the chameleon's appearance? Remember, with the black cells now reduced to minute dots, all we see is the yellow cells. The lizard is now yellow.

The situation becomes more complex if we put the lizard in bright light, on a white object where some of the "buttons" (actually receptors) in the skin are "pushed" or stimulated at the same time as those in the eye.

Now what happens? The "press-button" cells in the skin activate the nerve impulses that make the black cells expand. The lizard for a moment starts to become dark. At the same time, however, the "press-button" cells in the eye are "pushed" and they *stop* the changes that the skin cells (or "press-buttons") have started. Then no message is ever carried to the nerves that control the size of the black cells. The cells therefore remain small, so that we see only the yellow cells. To the unaided eye the chameleon is yellow.

Thus the chameleon with its colour changes is comparable to an electric sign that changes colour. But instead of wires and light bulbs of different colours, the lizard has minute nerves and tiny coloured cells. Instead of a number of press-buttons or switches, such as those that make the lights change in electric signs, there are special cells that serve the same purpose. We might even say that these press-button cells work on the same principle as the "electric eyes" now used for such purposes as opening doors. When the light falling on these "eyes" is interrupted, the doors open. But in the chameleon when light falls on the cells of the skin alone, the black cells start to expand and cover the white reflector cells, so that we see a green chameleon. If the chameleon's skin receives no light, the black cells remain tiny black dots, and the chameleon is yellow.

——Where Chameleons Are Found. Chameleons are most abundant and widely distributed in Africa and Madagascar, where they live both in trees and in shrubs. The "Common Chameleon" is actually no more abundant than many other African species. It merely happens to live in northern Africa, Israel, the Arab countries, and some of the islands in the eastern Mediterranean. Consequently, it is the kind most commonly obtained. Of nearly eighty species, only one is found outside the regions mentioned above—in India.

THE MONITORS

During Eocene times, some sixty million years ago, the monitors inhabited Wyoming, and doubtless other portions of North America. Today these animals are all confined to the Old World.

The monitors—they make up the family Varanidae—are agile, active creatures, whether on the ground or in trees, the two habitats most commonly frequented. Despite their well-developed limbs, monitors are quite snakelike in many features of their skeleton, as well as some of the soft tissues. The protrusible (darting) tongue is constantly in motion when the creatures are foraging, and doubtless serves to pick up odorous particles just as it does in the snakes. It is not impossible that the earliest snakes were derived from a burrower that branched off from the ancestral monitor stock. No burrowing monitors, either fossil or recent, have been discovered thus far, however. Should one be found, it would make an ideal ancestor for the snakes—if it were ancient enough.

The Giant Lizard of Komodo, *Varanus komodoensis*. It seems unbelievable that a ponderous creature nearly ten feet long could remain undiscovered until the present century. But that is just what happened in the case of the giant lizard. On the Indonesian islands of Komodo, Padar, Rintja, and Flores it had undoubtedly been known to the natives for centuries. But not until 1912, when a Dutchman, P. A. Ouwens, obtained five specimens, did the largest lizard in existence become known to the scientific world.

We can attribute the tardiness of the discovery of the giant lizard to the relatively recent exploration of the tiny islands between Borneo and Australia. However, the casual visitor might well have missed seeing the "Komodo Dragon", as the creature is sometimes called. Although it dwells in a region of bare rocks and broken ground interspersed with grass, bushes and an occasional palm, the giant lizard is a wary creature. Stalking through the tall grass with the long snakelike protrusible tongue working incessantly, it raises its huge body from time to time to scan the surroundings. Only by concealing himself behind a blind can the prospective observer hope to obtain more than a fleeting glimpse of this huge reptile.

Virtually nothing was known of the reptile's habits until W. Douglas Burden organized an expedition to study the "Dragon Lizard" in 1926. Mr. Burden found that the carcasses of wild hogs made suitable bait, and he managed to attract a number of the reptiles near the blind he had set up in advance. Hidden from the lizards, he obtained motion pictures as he watched them feed.

THE KOMODO DRAGON—GIANT OF THE LIZARD CLAN
Though the Komodo dragon of Indonesia is a large and formidable creature, almost ten feet long, it was unknown to science until the present century. Students of fossil remains tell us that sixty million years ago relatives of these creatures roamed over Wyoming.

——THE GIANT LIZARD IS A VORACIOUS EATER. Clawing and ripping with their sharp teeth, the voracious lizards ripped off great chunks of the foul meat. They gulped down each piece with head raised aloft and throat distended. A relatively small lizard swallowed the whole hind quarters of a boar at one gulp, hoofs, hide, hams, backbone and all. After feeding, each lizard licked its chops and rubbed both sides of its head on the ground as if to clean it.

Carrion can scarcely be considered the usual food of the dragon lizard, however. Mr. Burden suspects that it ordinarily preys on the wild hogs and small deer that live on the same islands. The larger meat-eating mammals are absent from the region, or were until the advent of dogs introduced by man. Free from competition from the higher animals, the giant lizard apparently assumed the role ordinarily filled by the meat-eating mammals. Individuals in zoos have been fed on rats and pigeons, as well as on hens' eggs.

Captive lizards kept in Java often ate their own eggs, which presumably are laid in the ground. A few eggs incubated in Surabaya produced young with yellowish bands on the tail and similar-coloured specks and larger circles on the body. The adults are uniformly brownish grey.

Relatives of the Giant Lizard. The giant lizard is actually one of the monitors. This family is represented by some twenty-five species living in Africa, Asia, and Australia, as well as many of the islands off the coast of Asia. Several other members of the family are large. Except for the crocodile, the Nile Monitor, *Varanus niloticus*, is the largest four-footed reptile in Africa. Individuals five feet long are not rare, and some even attain a length of slightly over six feet.

Nile monitors eat almost anything. They prey on birds, rats, snails, and insects, and also eat carrion. Like some of the monitors in Asia they habitually deposit their eggs in termite nests. The gaping hole left after the female deposits her eggs is quickly repaired by the termites, which do not bother the eggs. These incubate under ideal conditions, for the termites maintain relatively constant conditions of heat and humidity during the long period—nearly ten months—that the embryos are developing.

Interestingly enough the Tegu, *Tupinambis nigropunctatus*, a member of a distantly related New World family known as the Teiidae, has a surface resemblance to the monitors. It too deposits its eggs in termite nests, and in other respects as well appears to fill the same niche in South America that the Nile monitor fills in Africa.

THE SKINKS

The skinks are the most widely encountered of all the saurians. Nearly one-fourth of the existing lizards are skinks—the name is from an ancient Greek word latinized as *Scincus*, meaning lizard. Fewer than two dozen kinds live in the United States, whereas other parts of the world support a much larger proportion of the family (Scincidae). Skinks are abundant in Africa, Asia, and the islands of the Western

Pacific. But they are particularly numerous and attain greater sizes in Australia. Many of the limbless forms assigned to other families probably evolved from the skinks.

In the United States there are only three genera. One includes a single species, the Florida Sand Skink, *Neoseps reynoldsi*. This burrower, with only a single finger on each hand and only two toes on each foot, is confined to the sandy ridge that forms the backbone of the northern half of Florida. Another genus, abundant in Asia, also has only a single species in the United States—the Brown Skink, *Leiolopisma laterale*. The latter, as well as the sand skink, each have a transparent disc or "window" in the lower eyelid.

The Western Skink, *Eumeces skiltonianus*. The skinks of the genus *Eumeces* dwell in North America, Africa, and Eurasia. In the United States the only lizard reaching New England is the Eastern Skink, *Eumeces fasciatus*, which is found as far north as Connecticut. On the Pacific Coast of North America the western skink occupies the entire coastal region from British Columbia to northern Baja California. North of the desert regions, which skinks in the United States generally avoid, the range extends eastward to Utah and Montana.

ONE OF THE MOST COMMON KINDS OF LIZARDS
Skinks make up nearly one-quarter of the different kinds of lizards. The western skink pictured here is typical of the group, with its smooth, shiny skin and darting, forked tongue. This lizard has an unusually sharp sense of smell—useful in finding larvae that are buried underground. Although the animal is abroad by day, we do not glimpse it often.

Like most other members of the skink family, the western skink has flat, round, overlapping scales that are more or less of equal size over much of the body. These give the reptile a glassy-smooth shiny appearance. The upper surface is brown, with a bold light stripe extending on each side of the body from the snout to the base of the tail. Young skinks have a conspicuous cobalt blue tail. The name "blue-tailed skink" is common, although such blue tails are characteristic of the young of many other skinks. Moreover, as the western skink approaches maturity the blue colour gradually changes to pinkish brown.

——THE LIFE OF THE SKINK. Skinks are secretive animals. Though they are active during the day, relatively few individuals are seen unless logs or rocks are overturned. They prefer moist places, and are perhaps encountered more often in wooded areas than in the open. Like all members of the family, the western skink has a protrusible forked tongue, indicating that it has an acute sense of smell. Its food consists largely of insects and their larvae. It detects its prey by sight, but it uses its sense of smell to locate insect larvae buried in the earth or hidden under debris.

Many skinks bear fully-formed young, but the western skink lays eggs. Usually these hatch during July and August. The hatchling has a body about an inch long. It doubles its length the first year and attains the adult size of two and three-quarter inches during the third year. The normal life span has been estimated at about five or six years, the oldest individuals being about nine years of age.

THE GECKOS

The geckos are one of the larger families of lizards. Most, but not all, of them are small nocturnal creatures with claws as well as adhesive pads on their feet. Like other reptiles that forage at night, the majority of the geckos have eyes with vertically elliptical pupils. A very few of them, with round pupils, are mostly active in the daytime.

Geckos—they comprise the family Gekkonidae—may live in trees, rodent burrows, rock crevices, on the ground, or even in buildings. Some dig their own holes in the earth, although none is restricted to an underground existence. Geckos are largely insect-eaters; numerous kinds of insects are abroad, like the geckos, during the hours of darkness.

The Tuck-too Gecko, *Gekko gecko.* Nearly all geckos have a voice. It may be only a faint squeak, a chirp, or a clucking sound; or it may be a squawk, a crackle, or a loud cry that can be heard at a distance of a hundred yards. The shrill voices of the African Whistling Geckos, *Ptenopus garrulus,* are said to be well-nigh deafening when a number of them are calling simultaneously.

It is appropriate, therefore, that the name "gecko" applied to the members of the far-flung family should be onomatopoeic in origin: "Gecko" reproduces the sound made by the large tuck-too of the Indo-Chinese region. The tuck-too has habits similar to those of other members of the family, but it is one of the larger geckos with a body slightly longer than six inches.

It is one of the "house geckos". Like some of its relatives, it often lives in or around buildings. In southern Indo-China virtually every home or house of any size supports at least one or two of these large geckos. Making good use of the adhesive pads on their broadened toes, they run about on the walls, or even upside down on the ceiling. They accomplish this feat by means of tiny hairlike structures on the pads. These cling to irregularities in surfaces that are not so smooth as they look to the naked eye—suction is not involved.

——THE VOICE OF THE TUCK-TOO. The tuck-too does not call all year around. It begins in the colder part of the year, and continues calling until the onset of hot weather in May. During these spring months some tuck-toos call continuously, one after the other taking up the cry from house to house. Whether or not the call has anything to do with their courtship no one knows for certain. It is noteworthy that reptiles with a voice, the tuatara, crocodilians, and geckos, are all mostly active at night. This does not necessarily imply any connection with breeding activities, although the voice may help a gecko in finding a mate. The tuck-too uses its voice as a frightening device: when cornered it will utter a loud squawk as it lurches forward with its mouth open.

——WHERE GECKOS ARE FOUND. Geckos are particularly abundant in the Orient, as well as in Africa and Australia. There are several in Latin America and less than half a dozen that are native to the United States. This wide distribution points to the antiquity of the stock. Despite their diversification, which is exceeded only by that of the skinks, geckos are further remarkable in having adhered rather strictly to the ancestral habit of depositing no more than two eggs. They may bury them in the ground, attach them to walls, or lay them in crevices in wood or rock. As long as six months may be required for incubation. Upon leaving the egg, the young gecko immediately casts its skin and eats it. The only geckos known to give birth to fully-formed young are two species that live in New Zealand.

THE BANDED GECKO IS DIFFERENT

Geckos are small, night-prowling, insect-eating lizards that live in all sorts of places, mostly in the tropics. The banded gecko, which dwells in the American South-west, differs interestingly from the majority of geckos. Lacking the sticky foot pads common to most geckos, this one has claws that it can thrust out and draw in.

Adult geckos commonly devour their skin as soon as it is shed. Most of them are insect-eaters, although the tuck-too preys upon the smaller house geckos as well, and has been known to attack and devour small snakes. The Banded Gecko, *Coleonyx variegatus*, of the American South-west stalks its prey with all the caution of a cat stalking a mouse, pouncing on it with ludicrous ferocity. The banded gecko is catlike in some other respects, for it lacks the adhesive pads common to most geckos. It is equipped instead with retractile claws which it can thrust out and withdraw.

In the geckos, as in the iguanas, anoles, horned lizards, basilisks, Gila monsters, dragon-lizards, flying lizards, frilled lizards, chameleons, monitors, skinks, and others, we find that same amazing adaptability

that characterizes the lizards as a whole. It is not only the kinds
of lizard specializations that fill us with awe—it is also their variety
and versatility. But, in all the millions of years of their existence,
perhaps the most impressive example of lizard specialization came
when these creatures gave rise to a kind of "limbless lizard": the
snake.

Snakes—Most Recent of Reptiles

THERE ARE nearly three thousand kinds of snakes. Were
there only a few, we would undoubtedly consider them lizards with
interesting peculiarities. For that is essentially what they are: lizards
with special ways of existence that no longer require limbs as a means
of moving about.

However, several kinds of ancient lizards adopted burrowing habits,
and in the course of countless generations their limbs became smaller
and smaller until they were completely lost. The original lizard that
was to become a snake is believed to have gone through these stages
approximately a hundred million years ago. Other lizards went through
similar stages. It is not altogether certain that all reptiles now
classified as serpents are actually descended from the same four-legged
stock.

What usually distinguishes snakes from other reptiles is that the
two halves of their lower jaw are connected only by an elastic ligament.
Also, the brain case of snakes is enclosed at the front. Their eyelids
are not movable, their ears have no outside opening, and they have
no breastbone. Hip bones and even traces of limbs may be present
in snakes, although the latter are mere spurs noticeable only on careful
inspection. Snakes do not use limbs for locomotion. They make up
the suborder Serpentes ("crawling animals").

AN ARABIAN RACER

Swift-moving snakes, characteristically with large eyes, are among the few seen abroad by day in the desert.

A COBRA THREATENS TO BITE

The so-called snake charmers of Asia and the Middle East often resort to sewing the reptile's lips closed to stage such performances as this. *See page 1351.*

DEADLY HYPODERMIC NEEDLES

The hollow fangs of a pit viper are located at the very front of the skull, where they can be driven into the flesh of the victim by a stabbing action at the time of the strike. Fangs are shed and replaced periodically by others in various stages of growth behind them. *See page 1366.*

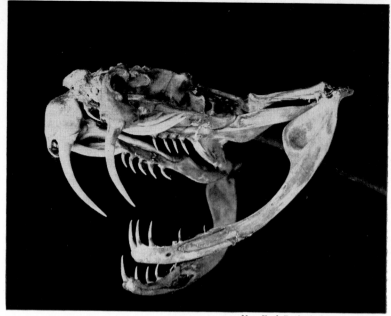

New York Zoological Society Photos

WESTERN DIAMONDBACK RATTLESNAKE AND NEW-BORN YOUNG

More human casualties result from bites inflicted by this rattlesnake than by any other snake in the United States. However, throughout the country, fewer than fifty people die each year from snakebite. Most bites do not prove fatal, even though no treatment is given. *See page 1379.*

Virtually all structures that are typical of snakes also occur in some lizards. This may be ascribed to the fact that various burrowing lizards have evolved along the same lines as snakes. However, snakes fulfil reasonably well the role for which their form fits them. The limbless lizards of today are probably comparable to the snakes in the early stages of their development. With snakes already on hand and occupying the various niches or modes of existence open to them, the field may have been pre-empted. Even though whole families of lizards are without limbs, members of these groups have achieved neither the habits nor all the structures of true snakes.

WHAT SNAKES FEED ON

It is interesting to note that snakes expanded as a group with the arrival of the rodents. The success of the snakes may well have depended upon the increased abundance of these small gnawing animals. The ancestors of the squirrels, chipmunks, rats and mice were probably the prey of the earlier snakes just as the rodents are today. Many of the snakes, such as the Bull Snakes, *Pituophis*, and the larger Rattlesnakes, *Crotalus*, rely largely upon rodents for their existence.

Nevertheless there are many specialists among snakes, as far as eating habits are concerned. The Hook-nosed Snakes, *Ficimia*, and their relatives, for example, eat almost nothing but spiders, the larger ones preying on tarantulas. The Florida Swamp Snake, *Liodytes alleni*, appears to restrict its diet to crayfish. Snakes in other parts of the world confine their diets to slugs. The Coral Snakes, *Micrurus*, most of them venomous and beautifully marked, definitely prefer other snakes, but they eat lizards on occasion.

One of the more amazing specialists is the Egg-eating Snake of Africa, *Dasypeltis scaber*. The teeth of this serpent are greatly reduced, but projections from the spine that actually pierce the throat serve to slit the shell. The snake swallows the contents of the egg and ejects the shell.

A few of the snakes that live in trees, notably some of the boas such as the handsome Dog-toothed Boa, *Corallus canina*, rely largely upon birds for food. Other snakes are not at all particular. King Snakes, *Lampropeltis getulus*, which range from coast to coast in the United States, with many subspecies, eat lizards, rodents, birds, and other snakes as well. Careful studies of a few kinds of snakes show that preferences may change in the course of a snake's growth. Juvenile rattlesnakes eat lizards, but adults of the larger species more often eat rodents.

In part the food of serpents with catholic tastes, as in many other animals, is dependent upon what is available. When inhabiting someone's garden, the Common Garter Snake, *Thamnophis sirtalis*, in the United States may live on a diet of earthworms. But under exceptional circumstances, when it lives in the vicinity of fish hatcheries for instance, the garter snake may well subsist on a fish diet. When it lives in wooded regions undisturbed by man, it commonly preys on frogs and salamanders.

THE REMARKABLE FEEDING TECHNIQUE OF SNAKES

Both the upper and lower jaws of most snakes, especially the lower jaws, are rather loosely attached. It is this peculiarity that enables snakes to swallow relatively large prey. As mentioned above, the two halves of the lower jaw are attached to each other at the chin by an elastic ligament. Each side of the lower jaw extends beyond the back end of the skull itself, where it forms a joint with another bone that in turn is joined to a small bone firmly attached to the top of the skull.

As the snake starts to swallow a large animal, it ordinarily selects the head as the starting point. The snake opens its mouth and thrusts it over the snout of the prey. The bones in the upper jaw contain teeth that curve backward—recurved teeth—in two rows on each side. The snake thrusts these bones forward, first one, and then the other. The lower jaw, with the right half widely separated from the left, moves in from below, aided by recurved teeth on each side. As the upper jaws pull the prey into the mouth, first one side and then the other is advanced while the teeth in the opposite jaw hold fast. Meanwhile the bone extending from the skull to each side of the lower jaw is swung outward and downward. This broadens the outline of the snake's mouth as it pulls the prey into its throat. Here the skin surrounding the neck is distensible, stretching to permit a large morsel to pass through it as the animal is engulfed.

The snake might have difficulty breathing during the engulfing process, which sometimes requires many minutes, were it not for a special provision. The front end of the stiffened breathing tube, which ordinarily lies back in the bottom of the mouth, is pushed forward to the edge of the lower lip. Once the prey has been drawn back into the digestive tract, muscles in the body wall tighten in front of it. A constriction or progressive tightening of the muscles carries the prey into the stomach.

HOW SNAKES KILL THEIR PREY

Whip snakes and racers simply seize small animals, such as lizards, and work their jaws over the head to begin swallowing it. But most snakes kill their prey prior to engulfing it. This they accomplish by means of venom or by constriction. Boas, king snakes, and many others move up stealthily upon a small animal, a mouse for example, which has attracted them. The snake, with its body drawn up in sinuous curves, suddenly straightens out the front part of its body, thrusting the open mouth forward with great rapidity. Its jaws close around the body of the prey, and at the same instant the snake throws several coils of its body around the struggling animal. The coils tighten steadily around the mouse. The hapless rodent seeks to breathe, but its lungs cannot draw in air because its ribs are held in a vice by the coils. Movements of the heart and the blood are brought to a standstill. The mouse suffocates, its life literally squeezed out of it. The snake brings death to its prey quickly and efficiently by means of this constricting method. But there are even more efficient ways of getting food.

Venomous snakes do not constrict. They rely instead upon the injection of a death-dealing substance that comes from glands in the head. The vipers, the cobras, and their relatives are the most advanced in this technique. Their fangs, which lie at each side of the front of the upper jaw, are really tubular teeth, very much like the hypodermic needles that doctors use, but curved instead of straight. The viper's head is launched forward with lightning speed. The instant the fangs are embedded in the flesh of its prey, muscles surrounding the gland tighten, forcing the venom through a small tube that carries it to the fang, and through it into the victim. In most instances, the prey succumbs in a matter of minutes, or even seconds.

It should be emphasized that venomous snakes use their fangs primarily for getting food. The fangs serve only incidentally as a means of protection, although the fangs of spitting cobras are specially modified for defence. Poisonous snakes are discussed in greater detail in the next chapter.

WHERE SNAKES LIVE

As you can see from this summary of their feeding habits, snakes are remarkably adaptable animals. They live in a great variety of places in nearly all parts of the world. The Common European Viper, *Vipera berus*, has even penetrated to land north of the Arctic Circle, in the Scandinavian Peninsula. Here it survives only because the region is near warm ocean currents. Snakes avoid cold regions, or those with short summer seasons. There are no snakes in Alaska and the more northerly parts of Asia and Europe, where the ground below the surface is permanently frozen.

Snakes are abundant in Australia, the only continent where venomous snakes outnumber the harmless kinds. Nevertheless no snake ever succeeded in reaching, or at least in establishing itself, in New Zealand. Some of the oceanic islands—those that never had any past connection with a mainland or continent—are commonly free of snakes. Nevertheless a few snakes have succeeded in reaching some small isolated land masses.

The Hawaiian Islands had no snakes until relatively recently, when the Indian Blind Snake, *Typhlops braminus*, appeared. Apparently it was accidentally brought to the island in some sort of produce. This snake is exceptional in its ability to survive and to perpetuate itself in some parts of the world where it has been introduced. It has now appeared in Africa, Cuba, and Mexico, usually near the coast. This suggests its accidental introduction through commerce.

WHY THERE ARE NO SNAKES IN IRELAND

There are no snakes in Ireland—but not because Saint Patrick drove them out! During the glacial epochs, over ten thousand years ago, the polar ice-cap pushed southward. It covered much if not all of Ireland and the larger part of England. It is doubtful whether any amphibians or reptiles survived in the British Isles.

When the ice-cap withdrew to the north, so much water is believed to have been frozen on land that the level of the oceans was lowered. England and Ireland were connected with the mainland. The English Channel was a river valley. Only a dozen of the reptiles and amphibians in continental Europe managed to reach England before it was again cut off by the rising seas as the ice-cap began to melt. Ireland, being farther from the mainland, was cut off first. Two amphibians and one lizard succeeded in reaching Ireland, but the sea had already separated it from England before a single snake could cross. Only three of the thirty-two kinds of snakes in Europe managed to reach England.

Snakes Without Poison Fangs

THE GIGANTIC CONSTRICTORS

ALL THE truly large snakes are either boas or pythons—and this holds for the past as well. But this does not mean that *all* boas and pythons are large snakes.

The boas, or members of the subfamily Boinae, are primarily inhabitants of the New World. Nevertheless there are boas in Madagascar; the Sand Boas, *Eryx*, live in some parts of Europe, Asia, and Africa; there are boas in the Malay region. The Rubber Boa, *Charina bottae*, adults of which rarely reach two feet in length, ranges farther north than other species. It is confined to the cooler forested regions of western North America, from British Columbia to southern California, and eastward to Montana. A second species native to the United States is the Rosy Boa, *Lichanura roseofusca*, which lives in the arid and semi-arid regions of the American South-west. All told, the constrictors make up the family Boidae.

Pythons, representatives of the subfamily Pythoninae, are found only in Asia, Africa, and Australia, with the single exception of the small Mexican Python, *Loxocemus bicolor*. Actually the differences between pythons and boas are rather minor. Both have telltale indications, including vestiges of hind limbs, that mark them as primitive. They are closely related members of a stock that must be at least sixty million years old. There appears to have been a general decline in size. Scanty as the fossil record is, it points to the existence of boas of greater dimensions in bygone eras.

GOLIATHS OF PAST AND PRESENT

The fossilized remains of a snake found in the Eocene deposits of Egypt, which consist of rocks laid down between forty and sixty million years ago, belong to a boa estimated to have reached a length of fifty feet! In rocks of similar age in central Patagonia Dr. George Gaylord Simpson discovered part of the skeleton of a large constrictor that he named *Madtsoia bai*. He believes that the creature represented must have been about thirty-five feet long and possibly more. Consequently it is reasonable to assume that still larger snakes of the same species once existed; for there is little likelihood that the single specimen uncovered would be the largest.

Few other snakes of great dimensions are known in the fossil state. However, in 1926 Professor J. Graham Kerr of the University of Glasgow in Scotland described what he believed to be the venom-conducting tooth of a huge serpent. The supposed fang, which measures nearly two and one-half inches along the outer curve, turned up in relatively recent deposits in the Gran Chaco of South America. No other parts of the animal were found. Assuming that the tooth belonged to a rear-fanged snake similar in proportions to the African Boomslang, *Dispholidus typus*, it has been speculated that the tooth indicated a serpent approximately sixty feet long. Such outlandish proportions can scarcely be attributed to a rear-fanged snake. The fossilized fang, if such it be, bears little resemblance to those of any snake now living. It may very well be a fragment of some totally unrelated animal.

Among present-day snakes the Reticulated or Regal Python, *Python reticulatus*, probably holds the record for length. Specimens twenty-eight feet long that weighed two hundred pounds have been well authenticated, and thirty-three feet has been suggested as the possible maximum. This snake lives in south-eastern Asia, the Malay Peninsula, and the adjacent islands, including the Philippines. The Indian Python, *Python molurus*, which ranges from Ceylon and peninsular India to southern China, is a smaller species with a maximum size of about twenty feet. A very close relative of the latter is the Rock Python, *Python sebae*, of Africa, with a verified maximum that does not exceed eighteen feet. The largest snake in Australia is the Queensland Python, *Python amethystinus*, reputed to attain a length of twenty-one feet.

TALL TALES ABOUT NEW WORLD SNAKES

There is little doubt that in the Western Hemisphere the largest snake is the Anaconda, *Eunectes murina*, of South America. Snakes of incredible size have been reported from Brazil since the earliest days of exploration. Lieutenant William Lewis Herndon, who traversed the country in the middle of the nineteenth century, heard stories of large serpents, and comments that it is "almost impossible to doubt"

THE ANACONDA—FAVOURITE OF TALL TALES

Twenty feet long or thereabouts, the anaconda is the largest snake of the Western Hemisphere. Though this monstrous reptile is the subject of many a tall tale, there is no first-hand report of an anaconda's doing away with a human being.

the account of Father Manuel Castrucci de Vernazza. Writing in 1845, this gentleman says that the snake called the Yacu Mamma or "mother of the waters . . . which I killed from my canoe upon the Pastaza (with five shots of a fowling piece) had two yards of thickness, and fifteen yards of length; but the Indians of this region have assured me that there are animals of this kind here of three or four yards in diameter, and thirty to forty long."

This should have been the story to end all snake yarns! Instead the story has been passed on and further embellished in recent years. An enterprising photographer in Brazil has distributed pictures of a large, evidently bloated anaconda that reputedly weighed five tons. The card depicting it states that it is eighty cm. (thirty-two inches) in diameter, and forty metres (131 feet) long. This misinformation has been widely accepted as fact. The identical photograph has reappeared at intervals over a period of a dozen years, each time accompanied by a totally different story.

A well-known newspaper account that appeared in 1948 describes a snake 156 feet long that was killed by a detachment of the Brazilian army. After a battle, during which the serpent "knocked down buildings —and upset motor-cars with its mighty bulk", according to the ridiculous story, the serpent was finally killed.

Although they have not been taken in by such weird myths, reputable scientists have been led to believe that anacondas forty feet long do exist. The truth of the matter is that even a length of twenty-eight feet cannot be fully substantiated. Too many measurements have been based on skins, which provide exaggerated notions of the size of the living animal. The skin of a twenty-foot anaconda might easily be stretched to twenty-eight feet. Interestingly enough, the length of the average large adult is approximately nineteen to twenty-two feet.

The Boa Constrictor, *Boa constrictor*, is so widely known that even its technical name has become a household word. It is commonly thought of as being "the largest snake". Actually it is exceeded in size by the pythons mentioned above, and it is only the runner-up in the New World. It is found in the lowlands of both North and South America, from northern Mexico to Argentina. Specimens exceeding twelve feet in length are uncommon, although larger examples are often reported. Dr. Colin F. Pittendrigh of Princeton has informed me that he measured one found in Trinidad that was eighteen and one-half feet long. This appears to be the largest one actually measured.

THE PREY OF PYTHONS AND BOAS

The available records indicate that the reticulated python preys upon comparatively small mammals—small, that is, in proportion to the size of the snake. Animals weighing more than one hundred pounds are seldom eaten by even the largest individuals. Major Stanley Flower, who lived in Bangkok where the reticulated python was abundant, even inside the city, states that such snakes make an easy living devouring fowls, ducks, cats and dogs. In Borneo they commonly eat young wild hogs.

The Indian python has a much more varied diet, being known to prey upon toads, reptiles, fowls, water rats, barking deer, and hog deer. One is known to have overcome a leopard having a body four feet two inches long, which it devoured afterwards. Colonel Frank Wall tells of a Chinese baby being eaten by a python on an island near Hong Kong.

The African rock python is readily maintained in captivity on a diet of guinea pigs or fowls, but we know little of its food habits under natural conditions. Mr. Arthur Loveridge reports the killing and subsequent examination of several rock pythons that had swallowed Thompson's Gazelles. He also gives one of the better authenticated accounts of a rock python's attack on a human being. A native woman living on an island in the south-west corner of Lake Victoria Nyanza was seized while she was washing clothes beside a stream. She was discovered dead in the coils of the python by a native who summoned men from the nearby village. They killed the snake, which was found to measure somewhat less than fifteen feet.

The reticulated python has also been known to attack and devour humans upon occasion. One that devoured a fourteen-year-old boy in the Dutch East Indies was captured and killed two days later, when the body of the unfortunate lad was recovered. Other cases have been reported, although relatively few have been fully substantiated. On the whole it is most exceptional for human beings to fall victim to pythons.

ANACONDAS

There are no eyewitness reports of anacondas devouring humans, although it is obvious that a large one could easily overpower an unarmed man. Anacondas are largely but not strictly water-dwelling in their habits, and it is likely that many of the larger South American rodents provide most of their prey. Captive anacondas have been fed on birds as well as mammals, and young anacondas are said to prefer fish. Franz Werner reports that one attacked a small crocodile temporarily placed in the cage with it. Perhaps caimans or crocodiles, which often share the anaconda's habitat, are eaten from time to time.

Boa constrictors occasionally devour rabbits in Sonora, Mexico, where they also make nuisances of themselves by eating young pigs and chickens. In Trinidad Mr. R. R. Mole found young deer as well as agoutí and ocelots in the stomachs of freshly captured specimens. In Paraguay, boas are reported to feed on rodents, and a "mountain cat" is known to have been devoured by one. Thus we see that most of the larger snakes have catholic tastes, with the smaller mammals comprising the bulk of their diet.

HOW SNAKES DETECT THEIR PREY

Many pythons and some boas have depressions known as labial pits in the scales bordering the mouth. These are readily apparent in the smaller kinds and quite conspicuous in some of the larger species. These pits, which are lined with nerve endings, serve as heat detectors, or special organs that enable the snakes that possess them to detect the presence of warm-blooded prey. Moreover, the paired arrangement of the pits provides depth perception. Snakes are able to judge their distance from mammals or birds, and to launch their biting apparatus with considerable precision.

Boas and pythons have eyes with vertically elliptical, catlike pupils, presumably adapted for seeing in dim light. The sense of smell, as well as sight, is used in locating food, but the heat detectors in the lips probably play an important part, leading to the actual seizure of the prey.

WHERE BOAS AND PYTHONS LIVE

Boas and pythons are largely night-time creatures. Most of them dwell in moist, forested areas. Those in dry regions are more likely to be encountered during periods of wet weather. I have found the rosy boa abroad and active on foggy days in San Diego County, California, when no other reptiles were on the surface. The only boa constrictors I have seen in their native haunts in Mexico, appeared during or immediately following rains. The Desert Boa, *Lichanura roseofusca gracia*, is largely nocturnal, although it is active at times during the early morning or at twilight. The Rubber Boa in California is evidently able to tolerate the low temperatures of its mountain home, where it is largely confined to moist forests.

THE BOA CONSTRICTOR SEEKS THE SCENT OF ITS PREY

The boa constrictor, pictured above, relies largely on its sense of smell to find its prey. Less familiar is the method employed by some of its relatives in detecting the presence of warm-blooded prey. Pits along the lips of some boas and pythons are so sensitive to temperature changes that the reptiles become aware of the presence of warm-blooded creatures at a distance of a yard or more.

HOW BOAS AND PYTHONS BREED

Boas, without any known exception, give birth to fully-formed young. Pythons, on the other hand, lay eggs. The mother coils about the eggs and remains with them until they hatch. The number of eggs laid depends upon the size of the parent, but as many as 106 have been reported for the reticulated python. Incubation takes from sixty to eighty days, during which time the "brooding" parent may have a body temperature as much as 6° Fahrenheit above that of the ground on which she is resting. Air temperatures may be considerably lower —a fact that has given rise to the misguided notion that the brooding python produces more body heat than it actually does.

LONG-LIVED SNAKES

The larger snakes hold most of the longevity records for snakes. This may be ascribed to the fact that they are more commonly exhibited in zoological gardens, the source of the few available records. An anaconda lived for nearly twenty-nine years in the National Zoological Park in Washington. Large snakes survive for long periods without eating—commonly for a year or two, as long as water is provided. According to Sir Charles Martin, one fasted for well over three years.

With proper care many snakes survive for long periods. Mr. C. B. Perkins, who is in charge of snakes in Balboa Park in San Diego, California, has been successful in keeping many kinds of snakes for a decade. Suitable quarters have been available only during this period, and most of these snakes are still living. The chances are, therefore, that Mr. Perkins will establish much greater ages for many species. It is probable that under natural conditions large snakes live for twenty or thirty years, or even longer. Mortality among juveniles is probably high, but a full-grown reticulated python or an anaconda has few known enemies except man.

OTHER NON-VENOMOUS SNAKES

In addition to the boas and pythons, there are several other families of non-venomous snakes. In fact, nearly four-fifths of the living species are essentially harmless as far as man is concerned. The vast majority of snakes do not possess fangs and are too small to attack a human being. Several families are made up solely of snakes without fangs.

THE BLIND SNAKES

Most members of this family are secretive burrowers, living underground or in decaying wood or vegetation, where they prey upon insects and their larvae. Some live in the nests of termites, the so-called "white ants", which are abundant in the tropics.

The blind snakes live in the extreme South of Europe, southern Asia, Africa, Australia and tropical America, including the West Indies. The smaller species have a wormlike appearance—though some of the large blind snakes of Africa are more than an inch in diameter and as much as two feet long. The blind snakes make up the family Typhlopidae.

As the name "blind snakes" implies, the eyes, which are scarcely discernible black dots beneath the polished scales on the head, probably do not function at all. Some of these snakes have traces of hip bones, others lack them completely. Except for a few representatives in tropical America that have a single tooth inside the lower jaw, their teeth are curved back and confined to the upper jaws. Some blind snakes lay their eggs, others keep them in the body until ready to hatch.

THE WORM SNAKES

The worm snakes are all slender burrowers, with mere vestiges of eyes. They resemble the blind snakes to some extent, but differ from them in having teeth only in the lower jaws. The worm snakes have traces of hip bones and hind limbs. We know relatively little about their habits, apart from the fact that they are insect-eaters. They comprise the family Leptotyphlopidae and are found in the American South-west as well as in the American tropics, Africa, and south-western Asia.

In the American South-west they are usually found under rocks or, less commonly, crawling on the surface at night.

THE SHIELD-TAILED SNAKES

The shield-tailed snakes use the snout for burrowing through the soft earth where they usually live—in mountainous or forested districts in peninsular India and Ceylon. These snakes are apparently aided in their burrowing activities by the fact that their jaws are joined to the bone supporting the snout; the bones of the skull are solidly united so that, unlike most snakes, the shield-tailed snakes cannot move their upper jaws independently. These snakes—they are all grouped in the family Uropeltidae—are small, seldom growing more than a foot long.

The tail ends in a peculiar fashion. In some species the tip is covered by a single large shield with ridges. On others the tail looks as though it had been sliced off at an angle, the resulting surface being covered with large, strongly keeled (ridged) scales—or by a single scale. Some scientists have suggested, without much evidence to support their view, that this "shield" serves as a sort of "burrow stopper", protecting the snake from attacks at the rear.

As far as we know, all shield-tails give birth to from three to eight fully-formed young. Captives have been fed on worms and the soft-bodied larvae of insects.

THE PIPE SNAKES

These are all secretive, burrowing snakes, with relatively small heads and short tails. Though they have characteristics of both the shield-tails and the boas, the pipe snakes also have structural peculiarities that set them apart from these and other families. As in the shield-tailed snakes, the upper jaws of the pipe snakes are solidly united to the skull.

These snakes also have traces of hip bones, and of hind limbs that end in a clawlike spur on either side of the vent—like the boas.

Relatively few species of pipe snakes are known. Most of them live in the Indo-Chinese region and in the East Indies, although a single species is found in tropical South America. The pipe snakes—they compose the family Anilidae—usually have reddish markings, and the South American Pipe Snake, *Anilius scytale*, is sometimes mistaken for a coral snake for this reason.

THE SUNBEAM SNAKE

The sunbeam snake—there is only one species, *Xenopeltis unicolor*, in this family—gets its name from its highly polished iridescent scales. It is a common snake in Burma, Siam, and southern Indo-China, where it occasionally exceeds six feet in length. Living in the earth, or beneath logs or stones, it comes to the surface at night to feed. It preys upon other snakes, frogs, and small rodents. In some ways the sunbeam snake combines the peculiarities of other families. But this single species —it makes up the family Xenopeltidae—is unique in having three scales at the back of the head where most snakes of the closely related families have only one pair.

THE COMMON HARMLESS SNAKES

Some of the best-known snakes in the United States—such as the racers, whip snakes, king snakes, hog-nosed snakes, bull snakes, water snakes, and garter snakes—are colubrids. In fact, throughout much of the world the snakes one ordinarily sees are members of the family Colubridae; the subfamilies make up two-thirds of all the snake species now living.

Several colubrids have grooved, but not tubular, fangs at the rear of the upper jaw. Although a few of them are capable of inflicting a somewhat painful bite, only one of the rear-fanged snakes is danger-ously venomous. The family includes snakes that live on the surface, and some that burrow beneath it. Others frequent trees, while there are some that are partly water dwellers, doing much of their feeding in streams, ponds, or marshes.

The Grass Snake, *Natrix natrix*, the most abundant snake in Britain, is also common throughout much of Europe, with the exception of the far north. On its home grounds this snake is retiring and un-obtrusive. If it is molested, it usually glides swiftly away. But if it is seized, two glands at the base of the tail give off a substance with a powerful and offensive smell. Many other snakes are equipped with similar glands, but few have quite so evil a stench as the water snakes.

Several races of grass snakes are now recognized, each differing in minor respects from the others. They all have keeled scales and blackish or greenish bodies. The most conspicuous feature of the variable pattern is a brilliant yellow or orange collar which accounts for the alternative name of Ring Snake—*Ringelnatter* in Germany and Austria.

——WHERE THE GRASS SNAKE LIVES. A relative of the American water snakes, the grass snake is usually encountered in damp, marshy districts. It may be seen on grassy banks or undulating fields—though its favourite haunts are old quarries in the neighbourhood of ponds and streams. The grass snake is an excellent swimmer, and we have many reports of its being seen at sea, often several miles from the shore.

In keeping with its water-dwelling habits this snake lives mostly on frogs, toads, salamanders, and fish. It evidently prefers amphibians, seeking fish only when other food is not easily available. It seizes and swallows its prey without first killing it.

——THE BREEDING HABITS OF THE GRASS SNAKE. Despite its close relationship with American water snakes, all of which give birth to fully-formed young, the European grass snake lays eggs. These it deposits in the late spring, in manure piles or any convenient collection of rubbish. Its eggs, anywhere from fifteen to forty, have been found in all sorts of places, however—in rotting logs, old walls, or any warm, moist vegetable material. Each individual egg is about the size of a pigeon's. The flexible whitish shells of the eggs often stick to the young even after they have slit the shell and departed.

Ordinarily the young hatch during the autumn. During incubation the eggs absorb moisture from their surroundings, becoming larger as the embryo develops. As with all oviparous (egg-laying) snakes, the hatchling is provided with a temporary, razor-sharp structure: the "egg tooth" at the end of its snout. This is used to cut the leathery membranes that enclose the embryo during its long period of development.

Grass snakes are hardy in captivity, and relatively easy to feed. The average size of an adult is about three feet. Exceptional individuals exceed five feet in length, rarely approach six.

——OTHER WATER SNAKES. Water snakes are plentiful in eastern North America, all the way from southern Canada to Vera Cruz in Mexico. Like the European grass snake, most of these snakes have a marked liking for water life; the eating habits of the two groups are very similar. However, some water snakes have a more specialized diet, limiting themselves more or less to crayfish. Other water snakes eat earthworms and slugs. In the neighbourhood of fish hatcheries the Common Water Snake, *Natrix sipedon*, becomes a pest, feeding as it does on the smaller fish. Under natural conditions it captures few game fish.

Throughout the eastern portion of the United States, water snakes are commonly mistaken for the venomous water moccasin. From a distance it is difficult to distinguish between the two, although along the Atlantic coast the true water moccasin is not found north of southern

Although they avoid some parts of the Southwest and the peninsular portion of Florida, the painted turtle and its four very similar subspecies are probably the most common and widespread chelonians in the United States. Like many turtle species, painted turtles hibernate and, at least in the northern part of their range, their emergence is as much a harbinger of spring as that of the first swallow. Averaging about seven inches in length, these little beauties like to sun on logs or limbs overhanging pools or streams, but it is almost impossible to approach without causing them to scuttle into the water.   *See page 1270*

[11-5]

[11-5A]

Smallest of the sea turtles, the hawksbills have considerable commercial value as the source of "tortoiseshell". Some individuals may measure a yard long and weigh 160 pounds, but they are the exceptions. Like all marine turtles, hawksbills inhabit tropical and semi-tropical seas and seldom leave the water—except for the egg-laying forays of the females. These two were found on the Great Barrier Reef off the coast of Australia.   *See page 1279*

Marine turtles have limbs modified into seal-like flippers, and all but one (the leatherback) of the six species still in existence have retained one or more claws, or nails, on the forward edge of the flipper. Powerful swimmers, their progress through the water resembles the flight of a hawk or an eagle. The green turtle, which ranges in size from 200 to 850 pounds, gets its name from the colour of its fat; the shell is olive or brown, mottled with yellow. Prized as an epicurean food item, the green turtle obligingly visits the shores of all continents, following warm ocean currents into northern latitudes. *See page 1278*

[11-6]

[11-6A]

Soft-shelled turtles are also considered excellent eating. Larger individuals may be 18 inches long and weigh 35 pounds and, with their long necks, sharp beaks and vicious tempers, require careful handling, Freshwater turtles with flexible, leathery shells, the 20-odd species of this family could be said to have world-wide distribution except for the fact that previously existing European varieties are now extinct. Most of the surviving species are found in Asia and the East Indies; there are several in Africa, and two or three inhabit the lakes, ponds and rivers of the United States from the Colorado River eastward. *See page 1276*

Virginia. Water snakes differ from the moccasins in having a round rather than an elliptical pupil, and in having a double row of plates under the tail. (The moccasin has a single row except at the tip.) Moreover, the moccasin has a pit between the eye and nostril—a structure never found in the water snake.

Needless to say, only the moccasin has fangs, but these may be folded back under a protective sheath of gum tissue, and in a dead snake must be prised forward for examination. Some of the common water snakes have rather large heads, sharply set off from the neck. Thus the shape of the head does not provide a reliable means of distinguishing harmless snakes from the venomous ones.

Water snakes—all members of the genus *Natrix*—are abundant in other parts of the world. Of more than four score species, somewhat more than half of them live in Asia and the adjacent regions, including the north coast of Australia. A few are found in Africa. There is a single species on the west coast of Mexico, and one that inhabits the brackish coastal waters of Florida has reached Cuba—probably in relatively recent times. Strangely enough, no water snakes are found in the United States west of the Rocky Mountains.

The Common Garter Snake, *Thamnophis sirtalis*, is one of the most widely distributed and most frequently encountered snakes in the United States. The garter snakes illustrate an interesting principle in Nature: when two or more species live in the same area, their habits are never identical. One may be less restricted to water than another, or they may differ in adult size or in food preferences—commonly in both. Usually they breed at different seasons. Careful studies have shown that closely related species in the same region are hardly ever in direct competition with one another. The same rule applies to virtually all other animals.

——WHERE GARTER SNAKES ARE FOUND. Though the common garter snake and its close relatives are limited to North America, they are quite numerous there. Every state of the United States, as well as each of the southern Canadian provinces, is inhabited by the common garter snake or one or more related species. Like the water snakes, the garter snakes have keeled scales and a disagreeable smell; but the garter snakes differ in having a single plate rather than a divided one at the vent.

Despite the close relationship between the two groups, the garter

snakes are less likely to be limited to the vicinity of water. The common
garter snake, with several subspecies, is found from the Atlantic to
the Pacific. In the East, it is the snake most likely to turn up in gardens,
where it preys on earthworms, salamanders, frogs, and toads. In the
West it is more often encountered in fields, or in bogs, marshes, and
the edges of creeks. It shuns the deserts, while the borders of such
streams as the Colorado River are the haunts of other kinds of garter
snakes.

——THE PROLIFIC GARTER SNAKE. All the garter snakes give birth
to fully-formed young. There are often more than twenty in a litter,
and large individuals may give birth to three times this number.
Seventy-eight is about the maximum. Garter snakes are among the
first snakes to emerge in the spring, and usually the last to retire for
the winter months.

By and large the common garter snake is not a very handsome creature,
most individuals being grey, with ill-defined stripes. A few, particularly
in the West, are patterned with olive green on the sides, with a yellow
stripe down the centre of the back flanked by red blotches. Patterns
vary quite a bit, however, not only from district to district, but even
within the same area.

The Eastern Hog-nosed Snake, *Heterodon platyrhinos*, is famous
for its bag of tricks. It makes a vivid pretence of ferocity, and it is
equally adept at playing dead. The hog-nosed snake is a stout-bodied,
slow-moving serpent, superficially viper-like in appearance. It may have
a pattern of squarish blotches, or a row of whitish circular markings
down either side of its back. Melanistic (uniformly black) individuals
are quite common in most parts of its range, and appear to be even
more abundant in the southern part of the United States. The average
length is about two feet; a length of more than three feet is comparatively
rare.

——MOCK FEROCITY. When encountered in the field the hog-nosed
snake is quite unlikely to glide away silently as ordinary snakes do.
It holds its ground, coiling its body as it inflates its lungs to capacity.
Approach it closely and it may hiss loudly as it strikes out boldly
toward the intruder. And if it is molested further, it may change its
tactics and flatten the entire front end of its body to form a sort of
"hood" not much like the cobra's, which is restricted to the region
behind the head. The hog-nosed snake continues to hiss throughout

these contortions. In the South it will often open its mouth, spreading its jaws wide as though imitating the water moccasin—also known as the "Cottonmouth" because of a similar display of the whitish lining of the mouth.

——PLAYING DEAD. If these antics fail to alarm the enemy, the creature still has one trick left. It contorts its body, writhing as though in agony. Then the snake rolls over on its back and lies perfectly still, the mouth agape and the tongue hanging out with dirt and debris adhering to it. The snake looks as though it had died a horrible death. Pick it up and it remains limp and seemingly lifeless, even if carried about. But place it on the ground right side up and it promptly rolls on to its back, thereby exposing its sham!

It is difficult to appraise the survival value of such behaviour, as we know little about its effect on enemies other than man. The ferocious gyrations are all humbug. The hog-nosed snake will not bite, no matter what the provocation! Even when it strikes, its mouth is closed. Nevertheless, it is widely feared, especially in the South. Its behaviour has gained it a fearful reputation perpetuated in such names as chequered adder, sand viper, puff adder, and spread-head.

The hog-nosed snake's upturned snout appears to be associated with digging tendencies, although this snake is not a true burrower. It preys almost entirely on toads, but it also devours other amphibians and an occasional bird.

There are two additional species; one, the Western Hog-nose, *Heterodon nasicus*, lives on the western plains, ranging from Montana southward to central Mexico. The other occupies a restricted range in the Carolinas, southward to Florida, with an extension of the range north-westward to Indiana. The western hog-nosed snake has a more pronounced snout than the others, and preys on lizards as well as toads and small mammals.

Like the majority of snakes in the United States, the eastern hog-nosed snake mates in early spring. In June or July it lays anywhere from eight to forty eggs that hatch in the autumn. The young vary in length from six to eight inches.

The Western Bull Snake, *Pituophis catenifer*, is of great value to man because of the part it plays in the destruction of rodent pests. The bull snakes and their eastern relatives—the Pine Snakes of the Atlantic coastal plain—are among the larger snakes ordinarily encountered in the United States. It is not uncommon to find individuals six feet long in the Middle West and in Arizona; a specimen seven feet eight inches long has been reported. Bull snakes are unbelievably abundant in farming areas. While crossing Iowa and Nebraska in the spring, probably during the bull snakes' mating season, I have come across more than one per mile dead on the road.

——THE BULL SNAKE AS A PEST EXTERMINATOR. Few other snakes, apart from the rattlers, are quite so important as killers of rodents. It is therefore unfortunate that bull snakes are fond of basking in such open areas as roads, where cars are likely to run over them. Nowadays some of the more enlightened farmers try to protect such snakes. The farmers realize that ground squirrels, pocket gophers, mice, rats, and other obnoxious rodents can be held in check more safely and easily with the aid of the bull snake than by trapping or poisoning campaigns.

On the other side of the ledger, bull snakes do some damage in game refuges, where they devour the eggs of ducks, quail, and other ground-nesting birds. On balance their destruction of rodents probably outweighs such damage. It may well be that the birds would fare even worse if rodents were allowed to multiply and compete for the seeds or plants consumed by the birds.

——HOW THE BULL SNAKE PREYS ON RODENTS. In the South-west the bull snake appears to be one of the few important enemies of the pocket gopher. These rodents commonly damage lawns and may even kill young trees. While I was living in Los Angeles a pocket gopher invaded my yard. Working underground, it ate all the roots from a small fig tree. Traps failed to catch it—but a bull snake evidently succeeded.

I freed the snake in the vicinity of the gopher as it worked on its burrow, carrying earth to the surface. The snake slowly approached the rodent, which seemed oblivious of its danger. When close enough, the snake suddenly struck. But the gopher ducked into its hole, pursued by the snake. I waited for an hour but neither reappeared. The damage to the garden ceased, and three months later I found the snake, sleek and fat, living in a nearby vacant plot where gophers abounded.

No doubt the rodent was killed underground. The bull snake in the Middle West is known to be capable of killing rats in their narrow tunnels by compressing them against the wall. Above ground, these large snakes are powerful constrictors, usually dispatching their prey in a matter of a few minutes before swallowing them.

Dr. A. F. Carr witnessed a fight between two raccoons and a Florida Pine Snake, *Pituophis melanoleucus*. The fight lasted more than an hour and wound up with the raccoons having much of the skin ripped from their noses, while the snake crawled away unharmed. In California I have seen a red-tailed hawk carrying away a large serpent that was probably a bull snake.

——How the Bull Snake Hisses and "Rattles". Bull snakes are equipped with a thin flexible membrane on the epiglottis (the thin plate of cartilage that protects the end of the breathing tube). Air forcibly expelled from the lungs causes this membrane to vibrate, producing a whirring noise along with the hiss. At the same time the snake's tail vibrates and its jaws spread while its head is flattened. It gains some resemblance to a rattlesnake thereby and doubtless frightens its enemies, regardless of whether or not they mistake the harmless bull snake for a venomous rattler. The loud noise has earned it the name "blow snake" in Utah. In California the same species is commonly called "gopher snake" for obvious reasons.

——How Bull Snakes and Pine Snakes Breed. The habits of the bull snakes and pine snakes are very similar. Both mate during the spring, and deposit their eggs in July. The young come out in the autumn, when they often appear in considerable numbers. The eggs, a little over two inches long, are usually buried in the ground. The snake uses its well-developed snout to dig or to push its way into the soil. The pocket gopher fails to keep such snakes from its burrow by filling the entrance with earth.

The Racers, *Coluber constrictor*, and **Whip Snakes,** *Masticophis flagellum*, are long, slender-bodied, fast-moving serpents. With their various subspecies, they range from the Atlantic to the Pacific coasts of America. Despite their specific name, the racers are not constrictors at all. The racer seizes smaller animals—usually by the head or neck; then, sometimes pressing the prey against a fold of its body, the snake "walks" its jaws around to the snout to begin swallowing. Racers eat almost anything, devouring insects, rodents, frogs, toads, lizards, and snakes. The whip snakes are partial to lizards, but they also eat small mammals and birds.

The racers in the eastern United States generally take to the trees to avoid capture. Whip snakes do this less frequently; they rely upon their speed on the ground. They are exceedingly swift, but their speed is somewhat illusory. Such obstacles as shrubs, rocks, or debris are no deterrent to these slender animals; in fact, a human being cannot out-distance a frightened whip snake on this kind of terrain. But if the snake is placed in the open, a fast walk is enough to keep abreast of it. The snake's maximum speed is probably no more than eight miles per hour—even when it is badly frightened.

Owing to the arrangement of the scales on the long slender body, the appearance of the whip snakes suggests the old-fashioned braided rawhide whip. They are sometimes called "coach whip snakes" for this reason. The maximum known length is eight feet two inches—recorded for the eastern whip snake. Racers are somewhat smaller, usually a yard or so long, rarely if ever exceeding five feet. The upper parts of adults are almost solid in colour: blackish, bluish, or greenish, depending on the region where they live. The juveniles are blotched, but this pattern changes to the solid colour during the first two years of life.

The King Snakes, *Lampropeltis getulus*, and the **Milk Snakes,** *Lampropeltis doliata*, and their relatives, are among the most successful American snakes. They are all constrictors, inclined to be secretive, and active at night as well as by day. Despite the fact that they eat a

THE KING SNAKE—A CANNIBAL

Constrictors that feed on other snakes, king snakes are famous for their ability to over-power rattlesnakes. However, they do not tackle the larger rattlers. Remarkably enough, king snakes are virtually immune to the venom of pit vipers.

wide variety of small animals, the king snakes are better known as enemies of rattlesnakes. They do, indeed, overpower small rattlesnakes, but rarely tackle rattlers that are not considerably smaller than themselves. Like other harmless North American snakes—but unlike lizards—they are immune to the venom of pit vipers. No one can say why the venom of rattlesnakes has no effect on king snakes.

It is doubtful whether any snakes are immune to the bite of true Coral Snakes, *Micrurus*. For these venomous relatives of the cobras subsist largely upon other snakes, and use their fangs to kill them. Where there are coral snakes, the milk snakes often resemble them in colour. For this reason the bright-coloured milk snakes are known as false coral snakes. The true coral snakes, confined to the South in the United States, ordinarily have red bands with yellow borders. By way of contrast, the false coral snakes have red bands with black borders. In New England, as well as in the mountains at least as far south as Virginia, adult milk snakes are usually blotched with brown and black and the belly is chequered with white.

THE MILK SNAKE MYTH

Owing to the fact that milk snakes frequent barns and stables, they have become victims of the myth that snakes suck milk from cows. Actually the snakes are probably attracted by the small rodents that abound in such places. In any event, snakes are incapable of extracting milk, and the amount that a milk snake could hold would never be missed by the most conscientious dairyman. Myths like this one go back to ancient times. In virtually every continent some unfortunate serpent that may actually be beneficial to man is designated as the "culprit".

——OTHER MYTHS ABOUT SNAKES. Another fabulous creature is the "hoop snake". There is a myth that this serpent can put its tail in its mouth and roll. In its most amusing form the myth states that the serpent's body can be launched tail foremost—like a javelin. Trees pierced by it are reputed to wither and die. It seems incredible that such nonsense should be taken seriously; yet the yarn is widely accepted. The Mud Snake, *Farancia abacura*, a handsome creature found in the swampy lowlands of the South in the United States, is sometimes cited as evidence. This snake has a stout, rather unusual spine on the tip of its tail. If the serpent is handled, it may press its spine on the skin of one's arm or hand. Although this action is quite harmless, the reptile is sometimes dubbed a "stinging snake".

Whip snakes, according to legend in some regions, can "whip a person to death". This fanciful notion arises from the snake's superficial resemblance to the braided whip, noted earlier in this chapter.

Even more persistent and widespread is the notion that snakes swallow their young to protect them. The young of some fishes do indeed retreat in time of danger into the parent's mouth. But the young of live-bearing snakes do not even remain with the parent. Apart from this, the evidence drawn from examination of thousands of captured snakes provides no support whatever for this yarn. There has not been one instance of a digestive tract that contained an entire litter of young snakes of the same species.

King snakes and other serpents are occasionally cannibalistic, and may eat their own kind—at least in captivity. But in this case too, no one has ever reported a litter of young in the digestive tract. The most likely explanation for the fable lies in the fact that live-bearing snakes about to give birth to their young are not infrequently killed. The young may be fully formed and quite active when, like Caesar, they are ripped untimely from their mother's womb. Although they are actually in the oviducts (the tubes that retain the eggs until they hatch), the incautious observer mistakenly believes that they must have been in the stomach. He is particularly likely to come to this conclusion if he has already heard the myth!

——OTHER AMERICAN COLUBRIDS. Pilot Black Snakes, *Elaphe obsoleta*, and their several relatives, the Rat Snakes, Chicken Snakes, and the handsome yellow and red Corn Snake, are among the common snakes in the eastern United States. The pilot black snake attains a greater length than the others; an unusually large specimen recorded by Conant and Bridges measured eight feet five inches! Like the water snakes, these snakes have relatives in Europe and Asia, but none in the far West of the United States.

The Green Rat Snake, *Elaphe triaspis intermedia*, and a few other members of the genus live in Mexico, including some of the arid regions. Though they shun the deserts of the United States, the most arid regions are occupied by a close relative, the Glossy Snake, *Arizona elegans*, a burrower widely distributed from northern Mexico to California and western Nebraska.

The glossy snake comes to the surface to feed during the twilight hours and night-time. The pilot black snakes and rat snakes are seen abroad during the day, and many of them are given to climbing trees.

They are all constrictors, partial to warm-blooded prey, with mice and rats as the chief victims. They also eat birds and young opossums and rabbits have been found in the stomachs of large individuals. Birds' eggs, lizards, frogs, and other snakes are less commonly included in their diet.

THE REAR-FANGED SNAKES

The rear-fanged snakes, termed *opisthoglyphs*, are not set off in a separate family or subfamily. Some species with fangs are obviously very closely related to others that lack fangs. Located at the back of the jaw, these specialized teeth are merely grooved on the front surface—they are not tubular like those of the front-fanged species, the cobras and vipers. As a rule the snake must resort to chewing action in order to insert its rear fangs and inject venom. Such serpents prey on rather small animals—usually lizards or frogs.

We do not know why rear-fanged snakes are more abundant in the tropics than they are farther north. Relatively few of them reach the United States. The Lyre Snakes, *Trimorphodon*, which get their vernacular name from the lyre-shaped marking on the head, are represented by three species in the South-west. The Cat-eyed Snake, *Leptodeira septentrionalis*, and the Black-banded Snake, *Coniophanes imperialis*, occur only in the extreme southern part of Texas. The Mexican Vine Snake, *Oxybelis aeneus*, a long, extraordinarily slender species mottled with grey, blends well with the twigs of the shrubs it lives in. Its range extends from Brazil to Arizona, barely north of the Mexican border.

None of these creatures is capable of producing a severe bite. The effects of the venom, though local, are sometimes painful. A much larger snake, the Boomslang, *Dispholidus typus*, found in many parts of Africa, can produce serious symptoms. Specimens exceeding five feet long are sometimes seen. Boomslangs have three sizable fangs in each upper jaw, behind from five to seven smaller solid teeth. The fangs are close enough to the front of its mouth to be brought into action fairly readily. The boomslang feeds almost exclusively on chameleons.

One entire subfamily, the Homalopsinae, of south-eastern Asia and northern Australia, is made up of rear-fanged snakes that live in fresh water.

There are very feeble grooves in nearly all the teeth of such American serpents as the Hook-nosed Snake, *Ficimia cana*, the Spade-nosed Snake, *Chionactis occipitalis*, as well as in the Black-headed Snakes of the genus *Tantilla*. Such snakes are termed *pleuroglyphs*. All of them appear to limit their diets largely to arthropods, scorpions, spiders, centipedes, and insects.

THE CAT-EYED SNAKE

The fangs of the cat-eyed snake are placed at the back of the jaw. Merely grooved in the back, its fangs are not so readily used as are the tubular fangs of cobras and vipers. The animal uses these specialized teeth mainly to kill frogs, its principal food.

In this chapter we have read mainly about snakes that are harmless, and in some cases even beneficial to man. We have seen that the generalized unreasoning terror with which these creatures are regarded has even been the genesis of myths that are sometimes fantastic, sometimes plain silly. The following chapter deals with some of the really dangerous snakes, such as the cobras, pit vipers, and rattlers.

Poisonous Snakes

THE POISON FANGS, and doubtless other parts of the venom apparatus of snakes, were perfected millions of years ago. Fossilized bones—including fangs—of a cobra that lived in France over twenty million years ago are virtually identical with those of the Egyptian Cobra, *Naja haje*, which today lives in large portions of Africa.

The cobras, like all other venomous snakes, are descended from serpents having solid front teeth. The ordinary snake's tooth is solid and recurved (curved back). Imagine such a tooth flattened out, with the edges brought together to form a tube; such is the construction of the fang. The joint may be seen on the front of the fang, with an opening at the upper end to receive the venom, and a smaller hole for its discharge above the pointed tip at the lower end. Thus the tube is lined with the same substance that forms the outside of the fang.

Actually, of course, the tubular fang is not the result of any flattening out or bending of a solid tooth. It is assumed, in the absence of a fossil record, that it evolved as a result of minor changes in successive generations over a very long period—many millions of years. The early ancestors presumably had mere grooves, possibly in several of their teeth.

In the course of time the two teeth at the front of each jaw became more specialized, and as these teeth became longer the groove in each became deeper. Eventually, in later generations, the edges of the groove came increasingly closer until they met. Once the groove was complete for the whole length of the tooth, the tubular fang came into existence—later to be copied by man when he devised the hypodermic needle.

NEW FANGS FOR OLD

The fangs, like the solid teeth, are shed from time to time. The hard substance of the fang, called dentine—is laid down in the soft gum tissue behind the socket that is to be occupied. The tip end of the fang appears first; it is then added to in somewhat the same fashion as a brick chimney is built. Behind each fang in use there are three replacements in progressively advanced stages of growth.

Tubular teeth at the front of the upper jaws in venomous snakes are always present in pairs, one pair on each side. One member of each pair is always solidly anchored to the jaw. The opening in the fang at the upper end of the canal is in close contact with the end of the tube or duct that leads from the venom glands located on each side of the head behind the eyes. When this fang is about to drop out, a fully-formed replacement moves forward into place in the adjacent socket.

For a few days there are two fangs present in the single jaw. Then the bony substance that holds the older fang in place is resorbed (taken up and carried away by the blood). The useless fang drops out or it may be left embedded in the prey and swallowed.

This rather elaborate mechanism for shedding and replacing fangs makes it possible for venomous snakes to keep their food-getting apparatus in excellent condition. They always have at least one usable fang on each side. During the period of growth the size of the replacement fang keeps pace with the size of the snake.

VENOM AND HOW IT WORKS

Venom glands are essentially modified salivary glands. They produce a special kind of saliva, the venom, that can cause the death of other animals when it is injected into their blood. Harmless snakes have similar glands but these produce a more or less ordinary saliva that would not produce serious effects even if they had the fangs to inject it.

Venom is an extremely complex protein compound produced by cells lining numerous small tubes inside the gland. Each tube is connected to other tubes and, not unlike the creeks flowing into a river, they discharge their venom into a main duct that leads to the base of the fang. As the fangs evolved from the simple grooved tooth to the hollow fang, it is probable that the venom became increasingly better adapted for the purpose of killing some particular sort of prey.

Rattlesnakes feed largely upon lizards and small mammals, which their venom quickly subdues. They rarely devour other snakes, which are not seriously affected by their venom, except in very large dosages. In contrast the venom of coral snakes, which commonly feed on other snakes, promptly kills such animals. (It also kills mammals, which are not eaten.) Most venomous snakes that have been tested are essentially immune to their own venom. No one has been able to discover why some animals are relatively immune when others are not. Presumably the answers will be found in studies of the complex chemistry of living creatures.

Venom exerts its deadly effects in various ways, depending in part upon the kind of snake that produces it. The venom of many snakes contains substances that cause the blood to clot or the tissues to be destroyed. Other venoms produce their most serious effects on the nerves, which stop working when the venom reaches them, and paralysis is the result. Thus, if venom reaches the nerves that control the muscles around the lungs of a mouse that has been bitten, it will suffocate because it can no longer breathe.

It should be emphasized that venom must ordinarily reach the bloodstream before it can cause any severe damage. Hungry rats have been induced to eat large amounts of fresh rattlesnake venom without showing any signs of sickness. The same amount of venom, if injected into the bloodstream would have killed scores of the same animals. It is doubtful, however, whether the same rats could have eaten cobra venom. As we shall see below, the venom of cobras is quickly absorbed through the eye, and it might as easily penetrate the tissues of the mouth or digestive tract. It is obvious, however, that cobras as well as all other venomous snakes habitually swallow the animals they have killed by means of their venom. It has even been suggested that the venom, like ordinary saliva, may aid in digesting the prey.

COBRAS AND THEIR RELATIVES

The cobras and their relatives include some of the largest and most dangerous snakes in existence, making up the family Elapidae. King Cobras, *Ophiophagus hannah*, exceed all venomous snakes in length, reaching a maximum length of eighteen feet four inches. The Black Mamba, *Dendroaspis angusticeps*, of Africa is a close second. Individuals ten or twelve feet in length are not uncommon and fourteen-footers have been reported. Some of the common cobras in Africa and Asia attain a length of more than seven feet.

The King Cobra, *Ophiophagus hannah,* because of its great size, can, when enraged, turn into an extremely ferocious and dangerous reptile. There have been many reports of unprovoked attacks on human beings by cobras. Fortunately, this cobra is not abundant, despite its extensive range throughout south-eastern Asia, from peninsular India north-eastward to southern China, and in the adjacent islands from the Philippines and southward through the Malay Archipelago.

The adults are usually uniformly brown or olive grey. Juveniles are black, with white, yellow, or buff cross-bars, chevron-shaped toward the front of the body. The pattern fades with increasing age, but the juvenile pattern is retained in some parts of the range until the snake has reached sizeable dimensions.

——THE LIFE OF THE COBRA. King cobras generally dwell in dense jungle, but Dr. Malcolm Smith reports that in Siam they are more commonly encountered in fairly open country. The generic name (meaning "snake-eating") is indeed appropriate, for, unlike other cobras, the king cobra restricts its diet almost entirely to serpents. It devours venomous snakes as well as harmless ones. Monitor Lizards, *Varanus,* are apparently the only known exception to this fare.

The king cobra is also exceptional in that it builds a "nest". This is little more than a heap of leaves or forest debris, presumably pushed into position by sideways movements of the reptile's body. The female deposits twenty-one to forty eggs in the bottom of the nest. She remains on guard, coiled in an upper compartment completely cut off from the lower. Occasionally the male is also on hand. The young are twenty inches or so in length when they emerge.

The reports of unprovoked attacks on human beings can, in all probability, be ascribed to the fact that people have unknowingly wandered into the vicinity of a guarded nest. There can be no doubt that large king cobras are occasionally aggressive—probably as dangerous as any snake in existence. However, their usual reaction to an encounter is to make off without delay.

The Indian Cobra, *Naja naja.* Few animals are better known throughout the world than the Indian or Spectacled Cobra. When the early Portuguese mariners visited India they returned with stories of the *cobra de capello* ("serpent of the hood"). The Portuguese name came to be so widely used that several related snakes with "hoods" have become known as "cobras".

————THE INDIAN COBRA'S TERRIFYING HOOD. Of the seven species that dwell in Africa or Asia, none stages a more magnificent performance than the Indian cobra. There are some cobras that are bigger, but few can dilate or spread the head to such an extent. The Indian cobra accomplishes this by raising and pushing forward the long ribs behind its neck. It stretches its elastic skin taut over the framework, forming a flattened area that may be almost four times as wide as the diameter of its body! The hood of some Indian cobras is ornamented with two joined eyelike markings—the "spectacle". Others have a white circle bordered with black, to form a pattern resembling a target on the back side of the hood.

Few sights are more terrifying to the uninitiated than the remarkable pose of an alarmed Indian cobra with a third or more of its body raised upright. Like the clucking and ruffling of feathers by a setting hen, or the rattle of the rattlesnake, the posture of the cobra serves the purpose of frightening the enemy. To add to the effect, the cobra generally hisses loudly when in this upright position. Furthermore, the cobra can strike from this position, inefficiently as compared with a viper to be sure, but dangerously enough.

————VENOM SPITFIRE. Far more effective when confronted by mammalian enemies is the "spitting" or ejection of venom by some cobras. This is purely a protective device, for the cobra kills its prey by biting and injecting venom. When it is confronted by what appears to be an enemy—even a human being—it sprays venom forward in two jets, one from each fang. The cobra deliberately aims for the eyes. No great accuracy is required, for at a distance of a few feet the jets break into droplets.

One drop in the eye is enough to cause immediate, excruciating pain. Unless the venom is removed immediately the structures of the eye deteriorate, resulting in permanent blindness. So rapidly is the venom absorbed through the delicate membranes that a single drop in the eye of a rat is sufficient to cause its death.

Spitting has been most often reported in the southern part of the Indian cobra's range, though, unlike two "spitters" in Africa, the Indian cobra is loath to eject its venom. Spitting, by the way, requires a special fang. The ordinary fang directs the venom *downward* from the poison canal in the same plane as the tip. The fang of a spitter is specially adapted to direct the venom *forward*, at a right angle to the point of the fang. Interestingly enough, the same modifications appear to have evolved quite independently in the Indian cobra, with varying degrees of perfection in the different subspecies. None the less, the fangs of the Black-necked Cobra, *Naja nigricollis*, and the Ringhals, *Hemachatus haemachatus*, in Africa are essentially like those of the Asiatic spitters.

——THE LIFE OF THE INDIAN COBRA. The Indian cobra is found throughout most of southern Asia, as well as in the Philippines and the Indo-Malayan Archipelago, as far east as the Celebes. It is equally at home in the jungle, in open fields, or around human habitations. It is not an aggressive snake, usually retreating when an avenue of escape is open to it. Mice, rats, frogs, toads, and—to a lesser extent—birds or other snakes are the principal elements of its diet.

The Indian cobra mates in January and February, but does not lay eggs until May or later. The parents tend to remain paired until the young hatch, one parent or the other guarding the eggs. As many as forty-five—though usually far less—are deposited in some hole in the earth. The hatchlings are ten to twelve inches long, and they more than double their length in the first year of life. By the end of four years they are nearly five feet long. This approximates the usual adult size, lengths of seven feet being rare.

The Egyptian Cobra, *Naja haje*, is famed as the imperial symbol of the Pharaoh Tutankhamen, whose tomb was discovered and excavated in 1922. This cobra is the largest of the seven species in the genus. Captain C. R. S. Pitman measured an Egyptian cobra taken near Lake Albert that was eight and a half feet long, and says that he saw even larger ones.

The Egyptian cobra, which favours warm, dry regions where water is available, is by no means confined to Egypt. It lives around the edges of the Sahara Desert, along the north coast of Africa, and southward through much of Angola and East Africa. A subspecies is found along the west coast of the Arabian Peninsula. The Egyptian cobra's hood is less spectacular than those of some other cobras.

The Black-necked or Spitting Cobra, *Naja nigricollis*, is a dangerous animal. Whether it reaches a length of seven feet is doubtful, but its

[11-7]

The true chameleons epitomize the adaptability of the lizards. All members of this family of nearly 80 species possess an extraordinary tongue which flicks out like a bull-whip to snap up unsuspecting prey; fingers, toes and a tail of remarkable grasping power; eyes that revolve independently in all directions, but which can be focused together at will; and—their best-known characteristic—the ability to change colour to harmonize with their surroundings. One species lives in India; the others are distributed throughout Madagascar, Africa and contiguous regions of the Near East. See page 1310

[11-7A & B]

The American anole of the more humid regions of the south-eastern United States is often sold at circuses and carnivals as a "chameleon" because of its ability to change colour from brown to green or vice versa. Actually its closest claim to relationship with the true chameleon is the fact that both are lizards. The anole may or may not match the colour of its surroundings, the change being effected by its body temperature and its exposure to bright light. The chameleon's change of colour is the result of a nerve reaction to the colour it sees closest to it. See page 1293

The "glass snake" of the central and south-eastern portions of the United States has a close relative in England and parts of Europe which is known as the "blind worm": they are limbless lizards with quite serviceable eyes and the peculiar lizard ability to shed the tail seized by an enemy and grow a new one. The glass lizard's tail when complete is considerably longer than its body, and may show some movement for several minutes after having been severed. Contrary to popular belief, the pieces of a chopped-up glass lizard will not reunite.

See page 1286

[11-8A]

The Florida worm lizard closely resembles a large earthworm (it averages 10 inches in length) and is blind and earless. It is the only one of its kind in the United States, but approximately 50 varieties are found in Africa and almost as many in South America. There is some doubt among naturalists as to whether these creatures are actually lizards, but at present they are so classified.

See page 1286

[11-8B]

The horned "toad" is distantly related to the anoles but whereas the latter live in trees or shrubs, this lizard lives entirely on the ground—and its coloration definitely conforms to its surroundings. Curiously enough, the body of the horned lizard is so constructed that it casts no shadow when the creature is sitting down. Twelve varieties are to be found from Kansas and Nebraska to the Pacific Coast, and from Canada down into Mexico; the only similar lizard outside this area is the "thorny devil" of Australia. The scaly projections known as the "horns" are more pronounced in the desert-dwellers than in the species that inhabit mountainous areas.

See page 1295

Iguanas are essentially New World lizards but some members of this rather large family are found in Polynesia and Madagascar. The numerous species range in size from one to six feet, and many of them run erect on their hind legs like some of their ancient fore-bears, the dinosaurs. For the most part herbivorous, many species spend a large portion of their time in the trees. *See page 1289*

[11-9]

[11-9A]

Nearly one-fourth of the existing lizards are skinks. They are especially abundant in Australia, where they grow quite large, but many species are found in Africa, Asia and the islands of the western Pacific. The five-lined skink is the common variety of the eastern United States; the lines are more distinct in young animals, and the brilliant cobalt blue tail is characteristic of the young of many species. There are 23 other kinds of skinks in the United States, ranging in size from two to six inches. *See page 1317*

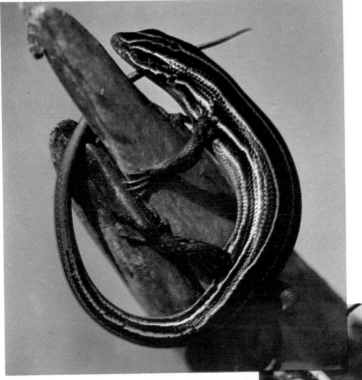

[11-9B]

Swifts are another extensive group of lizards which includes the scaly, fence and spiny lizards. They are the branch of the iguana family most commonly found in North America, ranging from coast to coast and from New York to Panama. There are about 30 varieties in the United States and about 90 in the southern part of their range, the largest of them being about five inches long. Primarily insect eaters, all swifts are good climbers.

See page 1293

The Gila monster is the only venomous lizard found in the United States. It frequents the desert regions of the Southwest, primarily Arizona and neighbouring states (with the exception of Calfornia) and northern Mexico. A very large one may be two feet in length. Like the skinks, Gila monsters have forked tongues. Their venom apparatus is used mainly as a defence weapon, the powerful jaws with sharp, grooved teeth being quite adequate for this lizard's food-getting activities.   *See page 1302*

[11-10]

[11-10A]

Beaded lizards owe their appearance to numerous, tiny round bones in their skin. There are only two species—the Gila monster and a Mexican species known as "escorpión", which is the larger of the two. Like the Gila, it has grooved teeth and a specialized saliva or venom.   *See page 1301*

[11-10B]

The chuckwalla of the desert areas of the Southwest, Northern Mexico and Lower California feeds on the flowers and fruit of cactus. The heavy-bodied lizard is about a foot and a half long and has an interesting habit of inflating itself like a balloon. It crawls into crevices for protection and, inflated, is almost impossible to dislodge.   *See page 1299*

smaller size is amply compensated for by its notorious ability to eject venom. In Tanganyika Mr. Arthur Loveridge observed a black-necked cobra that spat between a dozen and twenty times—all in rapid succession. Depending on the size of the cobra, it may spray its venom a distance of six to twelve feet. In some parts of Africa dogs occasionally return from a foraging expedition partly blinded after an encounter with a spitting cobra.

Theodore Roosevelt—like many African explorers who preceded or followed him—became acquainted with these cobras during his African travels. He was fortunate in not actually meeting a cobra face to face. Others have met it, and most of them lived to regret the experience. Washing the venom from the eyes with milk is the standard remedy. Water or any non-irritating liquid would probably be equally effective, though milk may be somewhat more soothing than water.

DISTRIBUTION

The black-necked cobra is widely distributed in Africa, mainly south of the Sahara Desert and outside the rain-forests. It is absent from the Cape region, however. Individual snakes from western Africa are sometimes jet black. In eastern Africa one of the subspecies is brick red, except for the black bar across the region behind the throat that gives this snake its name. Cobras of the same species with a slate-grey pattern are more widespread, although in Angola one population has black and red rings alternating through the length of the body.

The Ringhals, *Hemachatus haemachatus*, the smallest of the African cobras, is also the most highly perfected spitter of them all. Fortunately for those who dwell in other areas, the ringhals is found only in the south-eastern portion of the continent, especially the Cape region. It is a stout, relatively dull-coloured snake, with a white bar across the underside of its body below the hood. The well-developed snout of the ringhals gives it some resemblance to the hog-nosed snake of the United States. Like the hog-nosed snake, the ringhals sometimes feigns death. But the curious observer—unless he is equipped with goggles —must beware: close approach will invite the ejection of venom!

The ringhals, known to the Boers as the *spuw slang*, or spitting snake, erects as much of its body as the Indian cobra and displays an equally formidable-looking hood. The ringhals differs from other cobras in having keeled (ridged) instead of smooth scales on its back. The ringhals does not lay eggs but gives birth to fully-formed young.

Other African Cobras. The Yellow Cobra, *Naja nivea*, a non-spitter confined to the Cape region of Africa, is relatively small, and appears to be more primitive than others in the genus.

The Black-lipped Cobra, *Naja melanoleuca*, one of the larger kinds, with a maximum length approaching eight feet, lives in the African rain-forests. It shares its habitat with two forest cobras, *Pseudohaje goldi* and *Pseudohaje nigra*, both of which are largely tree-dwelling. Like their Asiatic relative, the African cobras subsist on a diet of small animals, with frogs and toads probably topping the list of preferred prey.

By way of contrast, the Water Cobras, *Boulengerina annulata*, which live in some of the African lakes, are fish-eaters. These are moderately stout and large, up to six feet or more in length. Greyish in colour, with black cross-bars, they bear a startling resemblance to a harmless water snake, *Cyclagras gigas*, of South America.

The Black Mamba, *Dendroaspis angusticeps*. Mambas are found only in Africa. Of five species that live in most of the continent south of the Sahara, none has a more sinister reputation than the black mamba. With the possible exception of the spitting cobras, no snake in the Dark Continent is so greatly feared. Mambas are all slender, swift-moving serpents, possibly, but not proved to be, faster than any other snake in the world. Speeds of thirty and forty miles an hour attributed to the black mamba are certainly gross exaggerations.

The fangs of the black mamba are located farther forward than in any other snake with immovable front fangs. The statement is commonly made that the fangs are exceptionally large. I could not substantiate this claim when I measured fangs and made some comparisons with cobras. In proportion to the length of the snake, the mambas have more slender but somewhat shorter fangs than the majority of cobras.

——Fact and Fancy about the Black Mamba. The yarns concerning this great snake border on the fantastic. People often endow dangerous beasts with the proportions and qualities of mythological monsters. The yarns about the black mamba are certainly no exception. "In a dusty country," according to one author, "its passage is marked by a trail of rising dust as its swiftness renders it practically invisible." The same man later comments more cautiously that "one could obtain a true estimate of the mamba's exceptional speed by practical test, though the writer can visualize no more suicidal form of amusement than that of deliberately provoking a large mamba in order to put it through its paces!"

In Rhodesia a black mamba is said to have created a reign of terror that lasted for three years, during which time it accounted for eleven human victims. Similar stories are rampant throughout most of Africa. Most of them can be taken with several grains of salt. The black mamba may well be the deadliest snake in Africa, but it could hardly be as diabolical as it is depicted.

At all events, attacks are reported to be more frequent during the breeding season. The black mamba is known to lay eggs, though we have no reports of a "nest" like that of the king cobra. Does the mamba guard its eggs? No one can say so with assurance; but if it does, we might be able to account for the aggressive attacks made without seeming provocation.

There may be truth in some of the gruesome statements about the black mamba. Others, such as that concerning the great size of the fangs, will not withstand scrutiny or investigation.

To conclude this account of the black mamba, here is another story with doubtful elements: Captain Pitman tells of a native who bore a grudge against his chief. The native tethered a black mamba near a path, knowing that the chief would use it in returning that night from a beer party. A white man discovered the dreaded reptile the following morning—too late to save the chief from the devilish intentions of his assassin.

Captain Pitman does not explain how the native managed to capture the mamba, nor how he ever succeeded in tethering it by the tail. Slender-bodied snakes usually manage to twist loose—at the expense of parting with the tail when occasion demands.

The Eastern Coral Snake, *Micrurus fulvius*, has two notable qualities. It is one of the relatively few dangerous snakes in the United States, and it is "cannibalistic", feeding on other snakes. The coral snakes are the only close relatives of the cobras in the Western Hemisphere. One of these, the Sonoran Coral Snake, *Micruroides euryxanthus*, is found in south-eastern Arizona and western New Mexico in the United States, ranging down into north-western Mexico. As for the eastern coral snake, it is found throughout Florida and northward on the Atlantic coastal plain to North Carolina. Westward it ranges along the Gulf Coast to southern Texas and Mexico. The eastern coral snake is rarely more than a yard in length, and adults of the Sonoran coral snake average about half this size.

———Coral Snakes in Mexico. Coral snakes are much more abundant in Mexico, which has several additional species. Many more kinds are found in South America, where the maximum size is five feet. Most—but not all—coral snakes are encircled by red, yellow, and black bands. All of them are secretive burrowers, rarely encountered on the surface. Ordinarily they are not aggressive. Maximilian, the unfortunate Emperor of Mexico, is said to have carried one in his pocket without ever realizing that it was venomous.

———Coral Snakes Can Be Dangerous. There have been cases of coral snake bites with serious effects, usually as a result of the victim's handling one of these creatures. Thus, Dr. Howard K. Gloyd reports the case of a woman in Texas who was bitten by one she seized as it crossed a road at dusk. She was acquainted with the local snakes, and did not hesitate to capture one that was obviously black. To her dismay it inflicted a painful bite.

Later examination disclosed that it was a melanistic (almost entirely black) eastern coral snake; the usual red and yellowish bands were absent.

Such abnormally marked snakes are of course the exception—as are albinos with their pink eyes and usually yellowish colour. Melanism, however, is not rare in some species of snakes. And as for albinos, they may turn up in virtually any population, though they too are not commonly encountered.

The eastern coral snake feeds mostly on other snakes. Occasionally it devours lizards. As far as we know, the Sonoran coral snake preys upon the smaller burrowing snakes that dwell in the same arid region. Little is known of the breeding habits of either species, apart from the fact that the eastern coral snake lays from two to four elongate eggs.

Relatives of the Coral Snakes. In Africa, Asia, and Australia there are snakes belonging to the same family; some are also known as coral snakes. Some of them are not appreciably different from those that live in North and South America. The chances are that they have been derived quite independently from stocks within the wide-ranging

Elapidae—the cobra family. Members of this family are absent from Europe and Madagascar, though they are well represented in Africa by the cobras and mambas, and by smaller species as well.

In Australia and New Guinea, where there are no vipers or pit vipers, the dangerously venomous snakes all belong to the family Elapidae. Australia, as we know, is the only continent where the venomous snakes outnumber the harmless species. The Death Adder, *Acantophis antarcticus*, said to be responsible for most of the deaths from snakebite in Australia and New Guinea, is superficially viper-like in appearance. The Tiger Snake, *Notechis scutatus*, of Australia is also famed as a killer.

SEA SNAKES

Though all the sea snakes are venomous, they are anything but aggressive. They are probably descended from the same stock that gave rise to the cobras and their relatives. The sea snakes' mechanism for injecting venom is similar to that of the land-dwelling front-fang snakes. Sea snakes—they make up the family Hydrophiidae—feed entirely on fishes, which they pursue at any hour of the day or night. Some have a definite preference for eels.

Few sea snakes wander many miles from shore, though all of them are excellent swimmers; their flattened, paddle-shaped tails increase the effectiveness of their sinuous movements in the water. (On land they are almost helpless—unable to crawl efficiently.) When a sea snake is under water, its nostrils are closed by means of a small flap or valve, but the valves open when it comes to the surface for air. Some species are fond of basking; however, they dive and disappear upon the approach of a boat.

Like moths, sea snakes are attracted by lights. A lantern held over the water at night has often been used as a means of collecting them. Few of them bite when picked up. In New Guinea, where sea snakes ascend some of the larger rivers, fishermen occasionally find them entangled in their nets, and fearlessly throw them out by hand. Elsewhere —in China—people eat these snakes. Bathers are never attacked by sea snakes, not even the largest ones, which are sometimes eight feet long. There have been fatalities only when large sea snakes were handled carelessly.

There are two subfamilies. One is of Asiatic origin, the other has evolved off the northern coast of Australia. Of more than fifty species, only the Common Sea Snake, *Pelamis platurus*, is widely distributed. It has crossed the Pacific and established itself along the west coast of North America, ranging as far north as Baja California. Westward this species has penetrated to the eastern coast of Africa.

Those in the more specialized subfamily, the Hydrophiinae, are strictly water-dwelling, and give birth to fully-formed young. Members of the other subfamily, the Laticaudinae, spend some time on land, where at least some of them lay their eggs. Sea snakes are also sometimes encountered in abundance off the coast of Sumatra and elsewhere. In his book *The Trail That Is Always New*, Mr. Willoughby Low describes how literally millions of these snakes assemble in a line ten feet wide and some sixty miles long! Dr. Malcolm Smith, the foremost authority on sea snakes, suggests that such assemblages may have something to do with their breeding habits, our knowledge of which is highly incomplete.

THE TRUE VIPERS

Some of the deadliest snakes in the Old World are vipers. Along with the pit vipers they have perfected the venom apparatus to a degree unsurpassed by other serpents. Each half of the upper jaw is greatly shortened and hinged to the skull in such a way that the fangs can be folded back against the roof of the mouth when at rest.

When the snake strikes, its lower jaw drops as its head is tilted backward and its fangs are swung forward. With the mouth open to an angle of almost 180 degrees, the fangs are in a nearly horizontal position. The forward part of the viper's body, which has been drawn back in sinuous curves, is straightened out at the same time that the mouth opens. This launches the head forward with considerable force, driving the fangs into the body of small prey. Some biting or chewing may follow the stabbing action.

As the fangs dig into the victim's flesh, the muscles surrounding the large glands back of the snake's head contract like a hand squeezing a syringe. This forces the venom from the spongy tissue inside the gland, driving the poison forward through the duct and the fang, into the wound.

Vipers replace their fangs in much the same way as do the cobras. The fangs of vipers are relatively longer and usually more strongly curved back, with no suture, or joint, to mark the closure of the venom canal. The true vipers comprise the family Viperidae.

Some vipers have unbelievably long fangs. Thus, the fangs of the six-foot Gaboon Viper, *Bitis gabonica*, can penetrate to a depth of an inch and a half. If the fangs of an eighteen-foot king cobra were as large in proportion, they would be four and one-half inches long! Such monsters have never existed, of course. Cobras cannot rotate their fangs to an inactive horizontal position, and this limits the size of their fangs. Consequently, as we have seen, an eighteen-foot cobra would have fangs little more than half an inch long.

THE DEADLY AFRICAN VIPERS

True vipers are limited to Africa, Europe, and Asia, including some of the islands in the Malay Archipelago. (They are absent from the Malay Peninsula.) They attain their greatest dimensions and diversity in Africa, where the infamous Puff Adder, *Bitis lachesis*, is quite abundant. On this continent there are prehensile-tailed vipers, *Atheris*, ground-dwellers of several genera, and also a widespread genus made up entirely of burrowers, *Atractaspis*. The latter are mostly glossy black or lead-coloured snakes, with small heads not set off from the body. Some are scarcely the diameter of a pencil, and little more than a foot long. Such creatures bear little resemblance to other vipers; however, their venom apparatus clearly identifies them with the viper group. They are quick to use their fangs with telling effect on an attacker. Presumably they kill the prey with their fangs, although nothing appears to be known about their feeding habits. They come to the surface at night or, after rains, during the day.

THE "SIDEWINDING" DESERT VIPERS

In the Kalahari and Sahara Deserts of Africa and the desert regions of Asia we find a number of smaller vipers that are curiously similar to the Sidewinder, or Horned Rattlesnake, *Crotalus cerastes*, of the American deserts. None of these vipers is closely related to the rattlesnake, nor have they rattles—rattlers are confined to the Americas. However, in their coloration, and the hornlike scale projecting over the eye, their general appearance is startlingly the same. Moreover, some of them have a specialized means of locomotion like that of the Sidewinder. All of them are admirably adapted for moving over the barren, sandy wastes where they live.

Their method of crawling is known as "sidewinding". The name is descriptive, for the snake's body does indeed move forward to one side of its head. It does not propel its body by the sinuous "swimming" movements that permit ordinary snakes to glide along, with each part of the body behind the neck region passing over the same ground. Snakes that sidewind literally roll along. The reptile raises its head from one position—with only its neck resting on the ground—and after bringing the head forward, puts it down again. The body follows, section by section, each being carried through an S-shaped path above the ground, to be rolled out on a track that continues from the neck.

THE SIDEWINDER—SNAKE OF THE DESERT

The sidewinder, or horned rattlesnake, a denizen of the American South-west, has a special method for advancing over the sandy wastes where it dwells. In effect, sidewinding involves an S-shaped motion by the snake, and leaves "snake-prints" in the sand.

Actually, the snake's body is in contact with three tracks at the same time, being raised from one and carried to the next. As the snake rolls along on fine sand it leaves a series of perfect imprints of its body. The tracks are parallel, with a hook on the end where the tail drags, and they lie at an angle of approximately 30 degrees to the direction in which the snake is travelling.

Other sidewinding creatures are the Sahara Horned Viper, *Aspis cerastes*, and the Phoorsa, or Saw-scaled Viper, *Echis carinatus*, which lives in the deserts of both Africa and Asia. The saw-scaled viper also resembles the American sidewinder—though it lacks the hornlike scale over the eye. The Asiatic Horned Viper, *Pseudocerastes persicus*, and the Kalahari Horned Viper, *Bitis caudalis*, probably also use the side-winding technique; unfortunately, we lack definite reports. The most detailed studies of this method of locomotion have come from observing the only American rattlesnake that habitually sidewinds.

The Gaboon Viper, *Bitis gabonica*, has been described as "frightful-looking" and "hideous". Quite as often it has been referred to as "beautifully patterned". According to Sir Harry Johnston, the colora-tion of this enormous viper "is perhaps more vivid and beautiful than in any other snake. It is like a carpet pattern of alternate black, greenish yellow, mauve, and buff; while, by the inflation of the body, white edges to scales are often shown."

Anyone who sees a Gaboon viper is properly impressed, regardless of whether he considers the snake handsome or repulsive. No viper surpasses it in length or weight. Pitman, who measured one five feet eight and one-half inches long in Uganda, is sure that some reach six feet. The one to which he applied the yardstick had a maximum breadth of over six inches, and the head was larger than a man's fist. The animal weighed eighteen pounds—with its stomach empty. The phenomenally large fangs have been mentioned earlier.

These gigantic vipers are largely restricted to forests, ranging over the whole of central Africa from the island of Zanzibar on the east coast to Togo on the west. The coloration of the Gaboon viper, like that of the American Copperhead, *Agkistrodon contortrix*, probably has camouflage value. The viper's head is pale brown, with two con-spicuous dark bands behind each eye. Purples and browns adorn the back. Such patterns, according to Mr. Arthur Loveridge, "render this handsomely marked snake difficult to see when among leaves in a sunlit forest glade".

Despite its huge size and potentialities for danger, the Gaboon viper is not an aggressive serpent. Bites are extremely rare, even among natives, many of whom go about barelegged and barefoot.

——How the Gaboon Viper Moves. In common with its more widespread relative, the Puff Adder, *Bitis lachesis*, the Gaboon viper is a sluggish, slow-moving creature. Like other thick-bodied venomous serpents, it rarely if ever crawls by means of sinuous movements of its body. It progresses with its body straightened out, or nearly so, using what is known as caterpillar movement, or "rectilinear locomotion". As its skin is loosely attached to the bony framework of its ribs and backbone, the snake is able to carry forward the broad scales on its belly in a series of waves. As the belly scales come in contact with the ground, they serve as a sort of anchor while the body is drawn forward within the skin.

The whole action is comparable to that of a cylinder inside a flexible tube.

——THE GABOON VIPER'S PREY. The Gaboon viper preys largely on rodents, including the Giant Rat, *Cricetomys*. In the Congo Herbert Lang captured a viper of this species that contained a rail (a bird) the size of a pigeon. According to Pitman, the Gaboon viper also devours frogs. It uses its huge fangs, of course, to kill such animals, striking with lightning rapidity despite its generally sluggish movements.

The prowling activities of this viper are largely limited to the hours of darkness; like all other vipers except the burrowers and the night adders, it has eyes with elliptical pupils. Vision is probably less important to this snake than its sense of smell, though it probably employs both to some extent in trailing or locating prey.

——BREEDING IN PRODIGIOUS NUMBERS. We know astonishingly little about the reproductive habits of the Gaboon viper. There can be no doubt that it gives birth to fully-formed young—probably the practice of all vipers, with the exception of the burrowers and the Night Adders. The related puff adder, which attains a length of slightly over four feet, produces fully-formed young in prodigious numbers— as many as seventy at a time, according to report.

The Rhinoceros Viper, *Bitis nasicornis*, belongs to the same genus as the puff adder, which is the widest-ranging viper in Africa and also occurs sporadically in the Arabian peninsula. The rhinoceros viper is a smaller species with quite an unusual pattern: a row of oblong blotches of blue down the back. Each blue blotch is enclosed in black, with a yellow line through the centre. Down either side there extends a series of connected crimson triangles bordered with blue. Toward the belly the markings are greenish, mottled with black. A black, almost arrow-shaped patch, surrounded by blue, occupies the middle of the head, extending on to the neck. Clusters of conspicuous erectile scales above each nostril are the clue to the rhinoceros viper's name.

This snake lives in wet swampy areas in the rain-forests of central

Africa. Its habits and behaviour are similar to those of its larger relatives. Smaller members of the same genus dwell in the Kalahari Desert in the south-western portion of the continent.

The Night Adder, *Causus rhombeatus*, similar in size and proportions to the American hog-nosed snake, has much the same feeding habits, with a definite preference for toads. Its viper status appears to be primitive. It has extremely short fangs, for example, and as an adult its venom glands are not confined to its head. The glands extend backward on to its body, just under the skin, with greatly extended muscles surrounding them.

The Northern Viper or Adder, *Vipera berus*, is the only venomous snake in England. (It belongs to the genus *Vipera*, which has seven European species and is also represented in Africa.) This is a small species, few of its members exceeding two feet in length. A light zig-zag pattern down the back is characteristic, though these markings may be ill defined or broken up into a series of dots. Not many people are bitten by these small European vipers; fatalities are rare. Vipers are rather abundant in some parts of England as well as on the Continent. During the spring, when they come out of hibernation, groups of several individuals are sometimes encountered.

Russell's Viper, *Vipera russelli*, is the best known and most widely distributed of half a dozen vipers in Asia. A length of five feet is not uncommon, and specimens six inches longer have been reported. There are no reliable statistics, but the "Tic Polonga"—as the viper is called in India—along with the saw-scaled viper, is probably responsible for more deaths than the cobras. It has been repeatedly stated that India has twenty thousand casualties a year from the bites of venomous snakes. The source of this statement dates back three-quarters of a century, and it was apparently little more than an estimate based on limited knowledge.

Fea's Viper, *Azemiops feae*, is one of the rarest snakes in collections. This snake retains some primitive characteristics, though its fangs are similar to those of the more advanced vipers. Fewer than half a dozen specimens are known; these are from upper Burma, southern China, and south-western Tibet.

THE PIT VIPERS

Pit vipers are the most formidable snakes in the New World. They surpass Old World vipers in length and probably at least equal them in weight.

None has fangs that approach the tremendous dimensions of the fangs of the Gaboon viper. An extraordinarily large rattlesnake eight feet long would have fangs seven-eighths of an inch in length—whereas, as we have seen, the Gaboon viper's fangs are an inch and one-half long.

This eight-foot monster might weigh over fifteen pounds.

Pit vipers—their family name is Crotalidae—are most widely distributed in the Americas. They are unknown in Africa, where true vipers abound, and they never reached Australia. They are relatively abundant in eastern Asia, from Korea southward. They also live in the Malay Archipelago as far south as the island of Timor. One species belonging to the same genus as the American Copperhead and Water Moccasin, *Agkistrodon*, ranges into eastern Europe, as far as the mouth of the Volga.

THE AMAZING PITS AND HOW THEY WORK

The name "pit viper" refers to the presence of a facial or loreal pit— a depression in front of, but below the level of, the eye. Its position varies somewhat in different species, but it is always present, and even more prominent than the nostril. On the mistaken assumption that the pit is a second nostril on each side, pit vipers are widely known in Latin America as *cuatro narices*, or "four nostrils".

Actually the pit is made up of two chambers, separated by a nearly transparent membrane. The forward chamber is the more obvious one. The other chamber lies behind it, with a hidden opening in front of the eye. The membrane between the two pits is richly supplied with nerve endings. Its similarity to the eardrum, which is lacking in all snakes, led to the erroneous suggestion that the pit vipers might have evolved a special hearing device on each cheek. In the absence of proof for this claim it was even suggested that such snakes had a "sixth sense"—something so foreign to human experience that we could not conceive of its use!

The experiments of Dr. G. K. Noble and A. H. Schmidt dispelled this dubious notion. In 1935 Dr. A. Ros discovered that the pits on the lips of several boas and pythons were the location of "heat receptors"—special organs used to detect the presence of warm-blooded prey. Taking their cue from Ros's paper, Noble and Schmidt tested blindfolded rattlers and discovered that, like the boas, pit vipers employed the nerve endings in the facial pits to ascertain the presence of mammals and birds. Blindfolded rattlers would strike with precision at warm objects, but seemed to be oblivious when objects of the same temperature as the surrounding air were held in front of them. They were able to detect very slight differences in temperature.

Thus, the pits are part of a highly specialized food-finding mechanism. They also enable the snake to direct the strike: depth perception, or the ability to gauge the distance separating the snake from its warm-blooded prey, is indicated. Blindfolded Copperheads, *Agkistrodon contortrix*, will follow every movement of a warm object moved in front of them—even at distances of five or six feet, depending on the temperature of the object. They never strike at it, however, until it is sufficiently close to be reached by straightening out the body as the head is launched forward.

The venom apparatus is essentially the same as in the vipers. There are no teeth in the upper jaws except the fangs, in paired sockets to allow for replacement on each side. As in all venomous snakes, teeth are present in four additional bones in the roof of the mouth. Behind each of the facial pits there is a hollow in the side of the bone that bears the fangs. This structure and the pit itself are the only important characteristics that distinguish the vipers from the pit vipers. For this reason some authorities prefer to consider the vipers and the pit vipers as members of subfamilies.

The Bushmaster, *Lachesis muta*. Three men trudged along a trail through the dense forest of the upper Amazon. Members of a crew making a geological survey, they carried their gear in packs on their backs. Suddenly the man in the rear felt an impact as something landed on the heavy canvas of his burden. Turning, he glimpsed the coils of a snake. Yelling with fright, he hastily withdrew his arms from the straps and dropped his pack on the ground.

As he and his companions whirled around, they saw a large snake, its squirming body held by the pack, its fangs embedded in the canvas. One member of the trio dispatched the snake with a blow from his machete. They examined the reptile and found it to be a large bushmaster, eight feet in length.

Such unprovoked attacks have given the bushmaster a reputation unequalled among American serpents. Like the king cobra in Asia and the black mamba in Africa, the largest of all the venomous snakes in the Americas occasionally strikes with fearless aggressiveness. Whether the bushmaster is truculent only when it is guarding its eggs remains to be determined.

Those who have been the victim of its attack have quite understandably been concerned with other problems!

The incident just described was related to me by Dr. Harvey Bassler, who spent more than a decade in eastern Peru. During that time neither he nor his helpers had additional encounters with bushmasters. These large pit vipers turned up sporadically, and in unexpected places, but never in numbers. Of some three thousand snakes assembled by Dr. Bassler, there were fewer than a dozen of the dreaded *verrugosa*, as the snake is known in Peru.

——WHERE THE BUSHMASTER LIVES. The bushmaster is known in forested areas from Brazil and Peru northward through Colombia, the Guianas, and Panama to southern Costa Rica in Central America. It may be more abundant in some areas than in others, but it is uncommon in nearly all parts of its range. Dr. Colin Pittendrigh informs me that while he was engaged in mosquito-control work on the island of Trinidad, the bushmaster was more often seen than any other snake. However, snakes are relatively rare—or at least not often seen—in the wet lowland forests where the large pit viper lives. Hence, this statement is not to be taken to mean that bushmasters were frequently encountered.

In Trinidad the bushmaster is known as the *mapepire*, in Brazil as the *surucucú*, and in Costa Rica as the *cascabela muda*. The latter name alludes to the bushmaster's lack of a rattle—in contrast to the Cascabela, or Neotropical Rattlesnake, *Crotalus durissus*. The name *verrugosa* ("warty") refers to the bushmaster's rugose skin. The scales on its back scarcely overlap, each being topped by a keeled tubercle. The upper side of the snake is light brown or yellowish, with a series of black or dark brown saddles, each enclosing smaller light spots.

——REPRODUCTION AMONG THE BUSHMASTERS. The bushmaster differs from all other American pit vipers in that it lays eggs. It shares this trait with some of the Old World members of the same family, however. The Asiatic species, *Trimeresurus monticola* and

Agkistrodon acutus, deposit eggs and sometimes remain coiled about them.

Egg-laying is a carry-over of ancestral habits. Live-bearing in most reptiles signifies a relatively simple advance, the eggs being retained in the body until the young are fully formed. In a few reptiles (possibly in more than we realize) there is a more intimate connection with the blood of the parent. Structures approaching, though not equalling, those of the placental animals are reported for some sea snakes, the anaconda, some skinks, and night lizards (*Xantusia*). (This means that the developing embryo in such reptiles is not wholly dependent upon the food stored in the egg yolk.)

If we knew more about the bushmaster's habits and habitat, we might be able to account for its egg-laying trait. Pit vipers that carry their developing eggs often bask. The heat obtained from the sun may increase the rate of development in the embryo. For such snakes as the bushmaster that inhabit dense forests, there may be no advantage in retaining the eggs in the body. The body temperature of a snake under such conditions is unlikely to be higher than that of the earth in a habitat where no sun ever penetrates.

Unfortunately such conjecture merely points to the need for additional information.

We know virtually nothing of the breeding habits of the bushmaster beyond the fact that it lays as many as a dozen eggs. Very large individuals may produce more. Eggs found in the burrows of armadillos and of the large tropical rodent known as the paca are presumed to be those of the bushmaster. Several captives have laid eggs, so that it is now certain that this is the normal method of reproduction.

We have had reports of bushmasters fourteen feet long, but this is nearly double the length of most adults. Consequently this reported maximum needs verification. Another specimen eleven feet long has also been mentioned, and Mr. R. R. Mole says that one he captured in Trinidad measured nine feet.

In captivity bushmasters have devoured rats, but more often they refuse food. Bushmasters do not thrive in captivity, and seldom live for more than a few months. They strongly resent being handled. When they are seized by the neck they often injure themselves as they lash their bodies about. The snake's neck is sometimes broken at the time of capture, and this further limits the number available for observation.

In comparison with rattlesnakes of comparable length, the bushmaster is a slender serpent. One from Trinidad that was slightly more than seven feet long weighed almost eight pounds. The fang of this specimen was nearly an inch long. The bushmaster is more agile in its movements than most pit vipers, but it is doubtful whether it strikes with greater rapidity than the rattlesnakes. However, those who have seen freshly captured bushmasters report that they are unbelievably quick, striking repeatedly at any moving object in their vicinity.

The Fer-de-lance, *Bothrops atrox,* owing to its wide range and abundance, is the most important venomous snake of the American tropics. It is known from Brazil and Peru northward through Central America to Mexico. North of the Isthmus of Tehuantepec in Mexico it is largely restricted to the Atlantic drainage, mainly the states of Vera Cruz, Hidalgo, San Luis Potosí, and quite possibly the southern portion of Tamaulipas. There are no definite records of this snake north of the Tropic of Cancer, however.

——THE FER-DE-LANCE HAS MANY NICKNAMES. The lance-shaped head gave rise to the name fer-de-lance, literally "iron of the lance", in the West Indian island of Martinique, where reports of this snake were spread by the French colonists. In Honduras the name *barba amarilla* ("yellow beard") refers to the yellow chin characteristic of most large members of this species. Costa Ricans use the name *toboba* for any of the venomous snakes with triangular heads, but the fer-de-lance is the "king toboba" (*toboba real*).

As with most wide-ranging species, the pattern and coloration of the fer-de-lance vary from place to place; there are further differences of detail within a region. Also there are changes that occur during the growth of an individual. Usually the adults are darker than the juveniles, often (but not invariably) with showy yellow markings. The velvety black of the skin is the source of another name, *terciopelo,* also used in Costa Rica. In parts of South America, the light X-shaped markings have resulted in the name *equis*—Spanish for the twenty-fourth letter of our alphabet.

Juveniles, which are more often seen than adults, have yellow tails. Hence the names *rabo de hueso* ("tail of bone") used in Mexico, and *rabo amarillo* ("yellow tail"), or even *rabo frito* ("fried tail"), used in parts of Central America. In Brazil adults as well as juveniles are called *jararaca*. Other names are *pelo de gato* and *toboba tiznada* in Central

[11-11]

The geckos are one of the larger families of lizards, being particularly abundant in the Orient, Africa and Australia. There are several species in Latin America, and less than half a dozen are native to the United States. The banded gecko of the Southwest lacks the adhesive foot-pads common to most geckos, being equipped instead with retractile claws. For the most part nocturnal animals, the geckos feed mainly on insects. *See page 1319*

[11-11A]

The granite night lizard is one of four species in the American south-western desert. A nocturnal animal like the geckos, it lacks movable eyelids, its eyes being protected with a transparent scale. Small to medium sized lizards, they make their homes behind loose rock splinters, and feed on beetles and other small insects.

Boas are primarily, but not exclusively, New World reptiles. The largest member of the family, the boa constrictor, is found in the lowlands of both North and South America. Two much smaller species inhabit western North America from British Columbia to southern California.   *See page 1327*

[11-12]

Pythons are found in Asia, Africa and Australia. One small species is found in Mexico. Many species of pythons attain a length of 20 feet, and some have been measured at more than 30 feet. Although boas give birth to fully developed young and pythons lay eggs, other differences between them are relatively minor. Both are nocturnal for the most part, and most of them dwell in moist, forested areas. The smaller mammals comprise the bulk of their diet.   *See page 1327*

[11-12A]

[11-12B]

Although the boa constrictor is generally thought of as the largest snake, it is not only smaller than the larger pythons but also takes second place in the Western Hemisphere, New World honours in this respect going to the anaconda of South America. All three are non-venomous constrictors. Average large anacondas measure from 19 to 22 feet in length. Chiefly but not strictly water-dwelling, anacondas feed mainly on the larger South American rodents; the young snakes have a preference for fish.   *See page 1327*

[11-13]

[11-13A]

The unusual behaviour of the eastern hog-nose snake of the United States has earned it a fearful reputation and such common names as "sand viper" and "puff adder" although it is a harmless, non-venomous reptile. A slow-moving, heavy-bodied serpent, it is superficially viper-like in appearance, and the lining of its mouth is white like that of the water moccasin—a fact the hog-nose uses to good advantage in its vivid pretence of ferocity. If its enemy refuses to be alarmed, this faker writhes through remarkable contortions as though in agony, flops over on its back and plays dead.
See page 1340

Racers are slender-bodied, fast moving snakes which, together with their sub-species and the closely allied whip snakes, are found throughout the United States. The blue-black eastern form averages four feet in length, and generally takes to the trees to avoid capture. (The whip snakes depend on their speed for safety, slipping easily among rocks and through debris.) They feed on small mammals, birds, insects, frogs, lizards and snakes.
See page 1343

[11-13B]

The rat snakes and their close allies the pilot black snakes (not to be confused with the black racer), chicken snakes and corn snakes, are common throughout the eastern half of the United States and have relatives in Europe and Asia. Fast, active snakes, they bite if attacked, but they are not venomous; they are all constrictors, and favour warm-blooded prey such as mice, rats and rabbits.
See page 1346

The king snakes are also constrictors, and inhabit most of the United States and Southern Canada. They are perhaps best known as rattlesnake killers, although they seldom attack a rattler their own size. (All harmless North American snakes are immune to the venom of the pit vipers.) Common king snakes average three and one-half or four feet in length. The eighteen inch scarlet king lives in areas frequented by coral snakes, and closely resembles them. The red king is commonly known as the "milk snake" because it is falsely believed to suck milk from cows.   *See page 1344*

[11-14]

[11-14A]

Bull snakes, which may be more than seven feet long, are most abundant in the farming areas of the Middle West. Powerful constrictors, they prey on mice, rats, ground squirrels and pocket gophers, and many farmers try to protect them as extremely valuable pest exterminators. Bull snakes are quite capable of killing rodents in their underground tunnels by pressing them against the wall.
     See page 1341

[11-14B]

Harmless water snakes so nearly resemble the venomous water moccasin that it is difficult to distinguish the two at a distance. If there is any doubt, close inspection is not recommended! The water moccasins are pit vipers, the small depression (the "pit") between the nostril and eye serving as part of a highly specialized food-finding and depth perception mechanism. They inhabit swamps, bayous and sluggish streams of the United States from Florida to eastern Texas, ranging as far north as the Dismal Swamp of Virginia, and up the Mississippi Valley to southern Illinois.   *See page 1338*

America; *mapepire balsain* in Trinidad; and *cola blanca* and *tepotzo* in Mexico. This list—by no means complete!—illustrates the need for standard scientific names.

——THE STRIKE OF THE FER-DE-LANCE. Unlike many rattlesnakes, the fer-de-lance does not raise its head above the ground in order to strike. Mr. Douglas March believed it could deliver the fangs as effectively from an extended posture as it could from a coiled one. It is not essential for a venomous snake to strike in order to embed its fangs and inject its poison. March could have vouched for this state-ment: he was bitten well over a dozen times by venomous snakes of different types while handling them at the Serpentarium in Honduras. He met his death as the result of a bite by a fer-de-lance.

——THE EFFECT OF THE FER-DE-LANCE'S BITE. Death does not invariably follow as the consequence of a bite from any snake. So many factors affect the situation that we must be wary of generalizing. If the snake's aim is bad, or if it strikes a bone, the fangs may glance off and inject relatively little venom. A large snake is likely to inject more venom than a smaller one. Other important factors are the victim's physical condition and his weight. Prompt first aid measures, especially incision and suction, may be of the utmost value in saving the life of a bitten person. At best, however, it is a harrowing experience.

The bite of a fer-de-lance, no matter how small, causes intense pain at the point where the venom enters the skin. This is followed by rapid swelling and discoloration. Systemic symptoms—those affecting the body as a whole—are delayed some minutes. Then a bloodstained, frothy sputum is discharged in great abundance. There are intense abdominal cramps, and a "tight" feeling develops in the chest. The victim finds it increasingly difficult to breathe. In severe cases death may ensue.

In Honduras Dr. H. C. Clark found that more people were bitten during the dry season than at other times of the year. (During this period the young of the fer-de-lance are particularly abundant.) The majority of the workers bitten were struck early in the morning during the first hour of work, usually by snakes with an empty stomach. Dr. Clark surmises that snakes unsuccessful during their hunt the previous night were still seeking food during the daylight hours.

——OTHER CREATURES PREY ON THE FER-DE-LANCE. During the daytime the fer-de-lance remains hidden. Often it selects holes in the ground for this purpose. In Honduras accumulations of dead leaves at the base of the manaca palm provide favourite hiding places. Yet armadillos dig out snakes from such hideouts, devouring them regardless of their venomous qualities. The rear-fanged snake, *Clelia cloelia*, called the *zumbadora* in Honduras, and the *mussarana* in Brazil, is known to seize an occasional fer-de-lance. Like the King Snake, *Lampropeltis getulus*, of the United States, the *zumbadora* has no particular preference for one snake over another—it takes whatever happens to be available.

The hog-nosed skunk of the American tropics has a reputation for feeding on venomous snakes, among them the fer-de-lance. The mongoose was introduced into Trinidad, St. Lucia, and Martinique with the hope of exterminating the venomous snakes. In 1930 Dr. Thomas Barbour reported the fer-de-lance to be very rare on Martinique, and he conjectured that the mongoose had helped reduce its numbers.

This belief appears to be unfounded. In 1944 the Agricultural Superintendent of St. Lucia wrote me that although the mongoose had multiplied exceedingly, there had recently been an alarming increase of the fer-de-lance in many districts. Studies of the food habits of the mongoose revealed it to be a menace to poultry and harmless native animals. Of scores of stomachs examined, not one contained the remains of a fer-de-lance!

——WHERE THE FER-DE-LANCE LIVES. The fer-de-lance is one of the serious hazards in the development of agriculture in the tropics. It dwells in woodlands, particularly in the vicinity of streams. The juveniles are likely to be tree-climbers, but the adults remain on the ground. In some areas they frequent banana or sugar cane plantations. While I was staying at the Hacienda La Oaxaqueña on the Coatzacoalcos River in southern Vera Cruz, one was killed in the yard a few feet from the house. Farther north in Mexico I found one on the Pan-American Highway in the mountains of Hidalgo. A car immediately ahead of mine ran over the snake as it was crossing the road just before midnight.

When I showed this snake to Huastecan Indians living at Palictla near the foot of the mountains, they insisted that the *rabo de hueso* was unknown in the lowlands. As the mountains receive more rain, the fer-de-lance in this region may be restricted to the uplands. In Honduras it may be largely confined to the humid regions bordering the Atlantic, being absent from the cloud forests at higher elevations to the south.

——THE PROLIFIC FER-DE-LANCE. The fer-de-lance is an extraordinarily prolific serpent. In Honduras a captive, six feet and seven inches long, gave birth to seventy-one young on 25 September, according to Douglas March. A fer-de-lance killed near the town of Progreso contained sixty-four young. Sixty-five were found in another that died in the Serpentarium at Tela in the same country. Mr. R. R. Mole reports that in Trinidad a captive gave birth to a litter, delivering three snakes on 30 September, and twenty-three the following day. On 3 October there was one more birth. All but one of the twenty-seven young were born dead, probably owing to the captive parent's poor health.

Mole states that the young were nine and one-half to ten inches long. Their failure to attain full size may have been due to the parent's abnormal condition. (Those born in Honduras averaged some thirteen inches in length.)

——THE SIZE OF THE ADULT FER-DE-LANCE. Among pit vipers the fer-de-lance is probably second in length to the bushmaster. Specimens longer than six feet are not uncommon in Central America, where this snake may reach greater dimensions than it does elsewhere. Ten feet has been given as the maximum, and there are rumours of twelve-footers. Whether the existence of such monsters can be proved remains to be seen; an individual much over seven feet may be considered large for a fer-de-lance. This snake is not heavy, tending to be somewhat more slender than the average rattler. The Honduran specimen, six feet seven inches long, weighed a little over four pounds after it gave birth to its huge litter. (The combined weight of the seventy-one offspring was over a pound and a half.)

——THE PREY OF THE FER-DE-LANCE. The young begin feeding soon after birth. Captive juveniles have been fed on small rodents, lizards, and small frogs. Dr. H. W. Parker of the British Museum states that a fifteen-inch specimen secured on Gorgona Island off the west coast of Colombia had eaten a centipede five and a half inches long.

Juveniles have a habit of wiggling their yellow tail, the body itself being of sombre hues and not nearly so conspicuous, especially against a background of leaves in their normal habitat. The moving tail

EAL / 11—H

serves as a lure, attracting small creatures to come within reach of the fangs. While feeding small frogs to young captives, Mr. Mole watched one of the frogs creep stealthily forward and seize the yellow tail in its mouth. Mr. Mole feels certain that if the young fer-de-lance had not been swallowing another frog at the moment, it would have turned and caught the frog that had seized its tail.

The tail of the adult fer-de-lance is coloured like the rest of its body. When the snake is excited its tail vibrates rapidly. Despite its lack of a rattle, the sound of the tapping on the leaves or the ground produces a certain amount of noise. This behaviour may have the effect of alarming the enemy, but it has nothing to do with capturing prey.

The adult fer-de-lance prowls at night, feeding on rats and other small mammals. According to Douglas March, the opossum is this snake's favourite food in northern Honduras. A fully-grown opossum was found in the stomach of a snake that measured six and one-half feet. The presence of feathers in the digestive tract of another snake indicates that an occasional bird may fall victim. However, so few birds are active on the ground at night that such prey must be highly exceptional for the fer-de-lance.

——How the Pattern of the Fer-de-lance Varies. Throughout its vast range in Latin America the fer-de-lance has basically the same pattern. But elements of the pattern emphasized in one region are less noticeable on individuals from another locality. Adults from the north coast of Honduras have a series of light-edged diamond-shaped blotches on the back, with black triangular areas filling in the space between the apex of one diamond and the next. However, the lower corners of each triangle are represented by a black dot, separate from the black apex at the upper end.

The yellow-margined black triangles meeting at the centre, with the two dark spots below, are particularly prominent in a specimen collected in the Mexican state of Hidalgo. The intervening diamond-shaped areas straddling the body are pale, with a pair of small oval black spots in each one. In some specimens from Nicaragua the yellow margins of the lateral triangles are quite noticeable on a dark background. Where the light margins of each triangle do not meet at the apex they stand out as series of inverted V's. Few of them run into each other across the spine to form X-shaped markings. In parts of South America the pattern of some specimens can barely be made out—though careful inspection usually discloses traces of the V's, X's, or diamonds, depending upon which markings are best represented.

Relatives of the Fer-de-lance. Over a dozen close relatives of the fer-de-lance dwell in Mexico and Central America. More than twice that many, some of them large, live in South America. A short, stout one, *Bothrops nummifer*, called the *mano de piedra*, is rarely more than two feet in length, but it is twice as thick as a fer-de-lance of similar length. The *tamagá*, or *tamagas*, corrupted by the English to "Tommygoff" and known scientifically as *Bothrops nasuta*, is rather widely distributed in Central America, Ecuador, and Colombia. Dunn's Pit Viper, *Bothrops dunni*, lives in southern Oaxaca in the south of Mexico. Natives gathering firewood near Tehuantepec are not infrequently bitten by these small snakes, though there are few casualties. The *toboba chinga* (*Bothrops lansbergi*) is a relative living in the south.

Some of the snakes in the same genus live in trees. The Eyelash Viper, *Bothrops schlegeli*, called the *bocaracá* in Costa Rica, is distinguished from others in having three scales projecting as points over the eye. These scales vary quite a bit in coloration in different areas. Some are brownish, others are green with pink cross-bars. Occasionally these snakes secrete themselves in bunches of bananas. A man was bitten in New York City by one that reached the United States in this fashion. An eyelash viper that we kept in captivity invariably held on to its prey when it struck—a habit that is probably shared by others that live in trees. If it released its fangs following a strike, a tree-dwelling snake would undoubtedly have difficulty locating its prey on the ground.

The Palm Vipers, *Bothrops nigroviridis*, are also tree dwellers, as their common name implies; but they are by no means restricted to palms. Some pit vipers living on an island off the coast of Brazil were given the name *Bothrops insularis* by the Brazilian herpetologist, Dr. Afranio do Amaral. He found them to be extraordinarily abundant in the trees, where they fed exclusively on birds. Amaral believes that drop for drop the venom of this snake is more potent than that of any other snake.

Some of the pit vipers in Asia are not unlike those in the Americas. Some also live in trees although others are ground dwellers. The Bamboo Pit Viper, *Trimeresurus gramineus*, and its near relatives are widely distributed in eastern Asia, from southern China and Formosa to the Malay Archipelago and the Peninsula on the east to India on the west.

During the Second World War, many American soldiers became acquainted with the Habu, *Trimeresurus flavoviridis*. This snake is fairly abundant on Okinawa, as well as some other parts of the Ryukyu Archipelago. It is a greenish yellow snake, with brown markings. The pattern is quite different from that of the fer-de-lance, but the body and head are startlingly similar. The habu attains a length exceeding five feet. Fully grown individuals are undoubtedly dangerous, although fatalities are apparently rare.

The Water Moccasin, *Agkistrodon piscivorus,* is the largest of three species belonging to a genus restricted to North America in the New World. Individuals more than five feet long are uncommon, but Wilfred T. Neill has reported a specimen from Georgia that measured approximately five feet nine inches. The venomous moccasin is unknown along the Atlantic Coast north of the Dismal Swamp in Virginia. Westward its range extends from peninsular Florida across the Gulf states to eastern Texas, and northward in the Mississippi valley to southern Illinois.

——THE WATER MOCCASIN'S APPEARANCE. The water moccasin's pattern consists of dark crossbands on a ground colour of brown or olive. The bands vary in number from ten to fifteen, tending to be wider at the base, and darker at the centre of the back. On juveniles the pattern is very noticeable. As the snake grows older the bands gradually disappear, becoming completely obscured in large individuals, which are almost uniformly slaty black.

——THE LIFE OF THE WATER MOCCASIN. The water moccasin has somewhat the same habits that we find in the more widely distributed Common Water Snake, *Natrix sipedon*. The two are frequently confused, as mentioned in our discussion of American water snakes. Moccasins are rarely found far from water. They live in swamps, bayous, and sluggish streams, often basking on the bank or on logs extending over the water. Along the edge of Payne's Prairie, south of Gainesville, Florida, they could be found in considerable numbers by overturning the piles of matted vegetation that accumulated around the edge of a shallow lake that had been drained.

On being molested the moccasin frequently stands its ground, opening its mouth and vibrating its tail. This threatening gesture exposes the white lining of its mouth—the origin of the name "Cottonmouth" commonly used in the South. The moccasin is partly a water dweller and swims with a speed that is astonishing as compared with the sluggishness of its movements on land.

Moccasins prey upon an unbelievable variety of small animals. They devour fish, frogs, small lizards, mammals, and birds with equal avidity. On one of the islands in the Gulf of Mexico, Dr. A. F. Carr found them waiting under heron rookeries, where they had eaten small skinks, eggshells, bits of fishbones, and other odds and ends dropped from the birds' nests.

The Mexican Moccasin, *Agkistrodon bilineatus*, ranges from Central America northward along both coasts of Mexico. In Sonora it is known as the *pichicuate*, but elsewhere it is called the *cantil*. Despite its common name, it is more like the Copperhead, *Agkistrodon contortrix*, in its habits. We know little of the Mexican moccasin's traits, but we do know that it is not restricted to the vicinity of water. A specimen from Sonora was found to have devoured a Blunt-headed Tree Snake, *Imantodes gracillimus*. The young use their yellow grub-like tail as a lure, holding it aloft and in motion.

The Copperhead, *Agkistrodon contortrix*. A very large proportion of the bites from venomous snakes in the eastern portion of the United States are inflicted by the copperhead. Fortunately it is not a large snake. Adults are usually less than a yard long, although a maximum of four feet five inches has been reported. Fatalities are uncommon, although the copperhead is definitely a dangerous snake.

——How to Recognize the Copperhead. The copperhead gets its name from the coppery, or reddish brown coloration of its head. It is a brownish snake, with some fifteen to twenty-five darker cross-bands. There are four subspecies that grade into one another. Those in the north, from Oklahoma and Kansas eastward to Connecticut and Massachusetts, have the cross-bands constricted at the midline to form hour-glass markings. Specimens from the South tend to be paler, often bordering on grey, with the cross-bands broken at the middle to form inverted V's on each side of the body.

In the area from central Texas northward through Oklahoma to south-eastern Kansas, the black cross-bands are well defined, with very little constriction in the middle. The belly of this race is not conspicuously dark, in contrast to a population in the Davis and Chisos Mountains of western Texas, characterized by a nearly black or heavily mottled belly.

Although the copperhead is found over much of the South-east, in the lowlands as well as the mountains to an elevation of at least four thousand feet, it is absent from peninsular Florida. Relatively few specimens have been taken in the northern part of the state.

The Common Milk Snake, *Lampropeltis doliata triangulum*, is often mistaken for the copperhead in the eastern part of the United States. The belly of the northern copperhead is usually mottled with grey or black, whereas that of the milk snake is marked with a chequer-board pattern of white and black squares. Close examination of the copperhead will disclose the facial pit, which of course is absent on the milk snake. Also, the copperhead has an elliptical cat-like pupil, a characteristic that readily distinguishes it from all harmless snakes north of Virginia.

——The Copperhead's Favourite Haunts. Copperheads are more often encountered in wooded or rocky areas. During the spring they may be abroad during the day. Hot weather usually leads them to change their habits and become night-time creatures. By day they secrete themselves in crevices, under logs, or similar places. During the winter months they assemble in fair numbers, occasionally in the same dens as those occupied by the Timber Rattlesnake, *Crotalus horridus*.

Copperheads mate in the early spring, April and May, the female carrying the developing eggs inside her body throughout the summer. Dr. H. K. Gloyd found that from two to six were born in August and September in eastern Kansas. Litters of from three to ten produced in the East at the same time are said to average a size about half again as large.

——The Copperhead's Prey. Few other snakes are quite so versatile in their feeding habits as the copperhead. The adults devour small mammals, but young copperheads readily eat insect larvae, particularly of some of the larger moths. One found in Pennsylvania was crammed with cicadas, probably taken as they emerged from the ground. A study of the eating habits of the copperhead in Virginia disclosed its preference for mice, shrews, and caterpillars. Elsewhere skinks and other small lizards, frogs, snakes, and birds have also been recorded among the animals eaten.

THE RATTLESNAKES

Long before the arrival of Columbus the rattlesnake had left its mark on the Indian civilizations of the New World. Rattlesnakes are depicted in the art of the ancient Aztecs as well as by the primitive peoples that preceded them. Dating back perhaps nearly to the advent of man in the New World, rattlesnakes have occupied a prominent place in the mythology and religion of various groups that penetrated middle America and inevitably came to know "the serpent with the rattle".

With the possible exception of the cobras, with their spectacular upraised body and spread "hood", no snake has attracted quite such universal interest and attention. None the less, the only truly distinctive character of the rattlesnake is the amazing structure on the end of its tail.

As pit vipers, the rattlesnakes share many attributes with snakes found in Asia and parts of Europe. However, rattlesnakes are found only in the Americas, where one kind or another inhabits much of the territory between southern Canada and northern Argentina. Rattlesnakes belong to the genera *Crotalus* and *Sistrurus*.

HOW THE RATTLE AFFECTS ENEMIES

The rattle is a frightening device. It is not used to warn the prey, for this would interfere with the snake's food-getting activities. Neither is it a mating call; the evidence available indicates that one rattler does not hear another. It serves a purpose similar to the spreading of the hood in the cobra, or the hissing of the puff adder and bull snake, namely to distract or intimidate an enemy. The effectiveness of the rattle depends, of course, upon the ability of other animals to hear it.

Rattlesnakes do not react in the same way to all enemies. They fail to rattle when approached or attacked by a king snake, for example. Under such conditions the rattler lowers its head, and arches its body, suddenly bringing it with force on the attacker as it approaches.

Weasels—and doubtless other creatures—recognize the rattlesnake as the result of the characteristic noise it can produce. Two California weasels that Dr. Raymond B. Cowles and I kept in the laboratory readily attacked and devoured lizards as well as snakes placed in the same cage with them. They even killed and ate large bull snakes, despite their loud hissing and ferocious striking. However, when a small rattlesnake was placed before the weasels they retreated and refused to come near it. The same rattlesnake, with its rattles removed, was again placed in the cage. This time the two weasels moved in without hesitation, severing the snake's spine with dispatch, and devouring the entire carcass.

A CLOSE LOOK AT THE RATTLE

The rattle is composed of a hornlike substance exuded from a matrix at the end of the tail. It is flattened from side to side, and the segments are formed in such a way that the main axis of the string is only slightly curved when the tail is extended horizontally. However, when the tail is raised, the rattle tilts forward, there being greater freedom of movement between the segments in this direction. Those at the end of the string are lost through wear. Strings much exceeding a dozen are uncommon—seventeen is the largest number I have seen. Slightly larger strings are reliably reported. Others of phenomenal length are the result of faking, since it is not difficult to snap several sets together. Rattlers living in rocky or brushy areas tend to have smaller strings than those inhabiting open country or some of the islands where rattlers are not often disturbed.

The rattle is made up of interlocking segments. Each impinges on the adjacent one as the tail is shaken at a rate that varies from forty-five to sixty cycles per second. The sound produced is not a rattling noise at all. On the contrary, it more nearly resembles the hiss of escaping steam—it has even been compared to the sound of bacon frying in a hot pan of grease. It may be much louder, however. A large rattlesnake can be heard at a distance of over a hundred feet. In small rattlers the noise produced is faint, resembling that of a buzzing insect.

A new segment is added to the rattle each time the skin is shed, with one exception. At birth a thickened area is present at the end of the tail. This is the pre-button, and it is lost when the skin is shed, usually within a few days after the snake has left the parent's body. This exposes the "button", a bell-shaped end on the tail. At the time of the next shedding the second segment of the rattle appears. This is composed of two lobes, one of which interlocks with the button. The next sloughing of the skin uncovers and exposes the first or forward lobe of the third segment. Behind this two other lobes interlock with the second segment. All subsequent rattles added to the string have three lobes.

THE EASTERN DIAMONDBACK—A DANGEROUS RATTLER

The eastern diamondback rattler, found in the south-eastern part of the United States, is the largest of the rattlers. Two other diamondbacks inhabit the south-western states, but neither is so large as the one in the south-east. Sometimes as many as one hundred rattlesnakes live together in one den.

The segments as they are added increase in diameter with the growth of the snake. Thus, if a string is complete, it tapers toward the button. During its first year a rattler may acquire from three to six rattles. The number depends upon the duration of the active season, and possibly the species, apart from individual variation. After they reach adult size in two and one-half to three years, rattlesnakes shed their skin less frequently. Consequently fewer rattles, all of them similar in size, are added.

In California's San Joaquin Valley Dr. Henry S. Fitch made an extensive study of a population of Pacific Rattlesnakes, *Crotalus viridis*, over a period of eight years. He found that adult female rattlesnakes in that region added only one rattle per year. Males evidently shed their skin somewhat more often, for they averaged three rattles every two years.

A male ten months old that Fitch marked and liberated in August was eighteen and a quarter inches long. It had two rattles and a button. Nearly five years and nine months later it was recaptured as an adult. It had an incomplete but tapering string of eight rattles. Comparison with other rattles indicated that about four or five had been lost. Had the string been complete the snake would have had twelve or thirteen rattles at an age of six years and two months.

WHERE RATTLESNAKES LIVE

Herpetologists recognize at least twenty-eight kinds or species; and, if we include the subspecies, we find that over sixty different names are applied to populations of rattlesnakes. There are more kinds in the American Southwest and north-western Mexico than elsewhere. Thirteen kinds dwell in the state of Arizona alone, and as many as six of these may turn up in a single locality. (At the Humbug Gold Mine in the foothills of Yavapai County in central Arizona, Mr. William Woodin, 3rd, and I found four different kinds in a single day's collecting at one place.)

Rattlesnakes occur in every state except Maine, and possibly Delaware (where they existed, but seem to have been exterminated) in the United States. They are absent from Maine, and such parts of New York State as Long Island largely because of their extermination in these areas. Only two kinds are known in South America, a relatively large one, *Crotalus durissus terrificus*, that is widespread, and a smaller one known only from the Venezuelan highlands. A close relative is found on the tiny Dutch island of Aruba off the coast of Venezuela. The Aruba Rattlesnake, *Crotalus durissus unicolor*, is smaller and greyish white, almost without any pattern in full-grown individuals.

Between Canada and Argentina rattlesnakes have been found in a vast variety of habitats, ranging from the tropical lowlands, arid deserts and plains almost to timberline at elevations approaching eleven thousand feet in the High Sierras of California. Some prefer rocky places, others dense vegetation.

RATTLESNAKES LARGE AND SMALL

Rattlesnakes range in size from small serpents less than two feet long to monsters more than seven feet long. However, a length of over six feet is uncommon, and an old record of the Eastern Diamond Rattler,

Crotalus adamanteus, given as eight feet, nine inches, is unquestionably based on a stretched skin. An exceptional giant may attain eight feet—although none so large, assuming it was ever captured, has been preserved.

Rattlers six feet long are not common, even in Florida, where the maximum size of seven feet, three inches for the eastern diamond rattler is authenticated. The same species ranges northward along the Atlantic coastal plain to North Carolina. Westward along the Gulf Coast it reaches eastern Louisiana.

Throughout much of Mexico, most of Texas, parts of Oklahoma and Arkansas, and the desert regions of New Mexico, Arizona, and extreme southern California, the Desert Diamond, *Crotalus atrox*, is the largest rattler likely to be encountered. Dr. L. M. Klauber, the foremost authority on rattlesnakes, quotes Mr. W. A. King of Brownsville, Texas, who says that he measured a specimen seven feet, five inches long that weighed twenty-four pounds. Outside Texas the same species rarely reaches six feet.

Next in size are some of the tropical species. The Mexican West Coast Rattlesnake, *Crotalus basiliscus*, is found from Oaxaca to southern Sonora. Its dimensions approximate to those of the desert diamond snake.

Large individuals are by no means rare, if I may judge from the frequency with which I saw enormous tracks on the road as I drove through Nayarit and Sinaloa in 1939. Evidently this snake is active principally at night: I saw the tracks early in the morning, but never the snakes that made them.

The region from Guerrero and Tamaulipas southward to Argentina east of the Andes, is occupied by two subspecies of *Crotalus durissus*. (The Central American race, *durissus*, is somewhat larger than the South American one, *terrificus*, with which it merges in Costa Rica.) The South American species has a relatively small head as compared with that of the diamond rattlers. The maximum body size of the species is slightly under six feet. Interestingly enough, the venom of this rattler with the southernmost distribution is appreciably different from that of the North American rattlers.

Other large rattlers in the United States include the Canebrake Rattlesnake, *Crotalus horridus atricaudus*, the southern subspecies of the Timber Rattlesnake, *Crotalus horridus horridus*, that lives in most of the United States from the Mississippi valley eastward. The Red

Diamond Rattler, *Crotalus ruber*, is a large species, occasionally over five feet, that is limited to the extreme south-western corner of California in the United States. It also dwells in nearly all of the peninsula of Baja California, where a race, *Crotalus ruber lucasensis*, at the southern extremity resembles the desert diamond.

Three species of small rattlers are referred to a separate genus, *Sistrurus*, members of which are called Ground Rattlers. They all have large symmetrically arranged plates covering the front of the head where other rattlers have numerous small scales. The largest of the group is the Massasauga, *Sistrurus catenatus*, which attains a length of nearly a yard. One of the smallest is the Carolina Ground Rattler, *Sistrurus miliarus miliarus*, which is rarely over two feet.

The smallest species in the genus *Crotalus*, and also the rarest of all rattlesnakes, is the Long-tailed Rattlesnake, *Crotalus stejnegeri*. Its range is limited to the mountains of eastern Sinaloa and western Durango in Mexico. Collectors seldom visit this region, and they may eventually find this tiny rattler to be more abundant than our present information indicates. We know of only five specimens, all of them less than two feet long.

THE PREY OF RATTLESNAKES

The larger species, particularly the diamond rattlers, prey mostly upon rabbits. In Florida the eastern diamond's favourite food is the swamp rabbit. Ground squirrels, prairie dogs, gophers, and various rodents lumped under the terms "rats" and "mice" are the chief food of adult rattlesnakes in many areas.

One of the most detailed studies of feeding habits in snakes was carried out by Dr. Henry S. Fitch. He dealt with a population of the Pacific Rattlesnake, a moderately large species with a maximum length of four and one-half feet. In San Joaquin Valley, where Dr. Fitch worked, he found these rattlers to be feeding on nineteen kinds of prey. Ground squirrels topped the list, comprising well over half the food the snakes had eaten. Cottontails were second, making up nearly one-fifth of the diet. Kangaroo rats, pocket gophers, wood rats, and seven kinds of mice follow, with one chipmunk, a few lizards, three kinds of birds, and one tailless amphibian making up the remainder of the food consumed.

Elsewhere the same species of rattlesnake might have a totally different diet. Juvenile Pacific rattlesnakes, as well as the smaller species, often kill lizards, which comprise a large proportion of their prey in some regions. Fitch estimates that an amount of food at least twice the weight of the snake is necessary to maintain it during the growing season. It is probable that most rattlers feed approximately every week or ten days during the period of the year when they are active.

MORE RATTLERS THAN WE THINK

There can be little doubt that rattlesnakes are present in greater numbers in many areas than one might expect from casual observations. Owing to their secretive habits relatively few are likely to be seen. In the area where Dr. Fitch worked, he calculated that rattlesnakes were slightly more numerous than one to the acre. Other regions undoubtedly support fewer or more, depending upon the available food supply. This in turn may be governed by competition with mammals or birds that prey upon the same rodents or other animals eaten by rattlesnakes.

Rattlesnakes that dwell in regions with cold winters often assemble in dens. The site they choose may be a natural cleft in a cliff or hillside, or it may be in the burrow or burrows of some kind of animal. On the Great Plains the rattlers often use the holes dug by prairie dogs. Rattlesnakes retire to these winter quarters in the autumn, commonly in October, and do not come out until March or April. The number found in any one den depends upon many factors, including the amount of space available to house the assemblage. Often there are well over a hundred rattlers in a single den.

THE RATTLESNAKE'S ENEMIES

Despite their efficient means of defence, rattlesnakes are killed or preyed upon by a number of enemies. Human beings, of course, rarely miss an opportunity to kill a rattler. Such birds as hawks, owls, ravens, and road runners kill a few rattlers. Dr. Fitch found that red-tailed hawks and coyotes were among the more important natural enemies of the Pacific rattlesnake in the region where he studied the species.

King snakes were not plentiful in the area, but elsewhere they attack rattlesnakes—usually the smaller ones. A king snake collected in California disgorged three juvenile rattlesnakes. The racers and other snakes also prey on small rattlers. The adults, especially of the larger rattlesnakes, are naturally far less vulnerable than the juveniles.

HOOFED ENEMIES

Some of the hoofed animals, including the pronghorn, deer, and goats are known to kill rattlers by trampling on them. An occasional horse may—the claim is often made that they do—but certainly the majority of them do not react at all to the rattlesnake. In my experience the only horses that paid the slightest attention to a rattler were those that shied at such objects as a scrap of paper carried in the breeze. On several occasions I have carried live rattlesnakes while on horseback without the horse manifesting any concern.

HOW RATTLESNAKES BREED

In the Temperate Zone most rattlesnakes mate during the spring. A few have been found paired during the fall. The young are born during the late summer or autumn. The broods vary in size, there being as few as two or as many as thirty or more in a single litter. Dr. Fitch found that Pacific rattlesnakes contained from five to thirty-three eggs, not all of which may have been fertile. He believes that in this species the average litter comprises about ten. Average litter size varies from species to species.

In the United States female rattlesnakes attain the breeding size in about two and a half years. Thereafter those in the warmer regions ordinarily produce a litter every year. In the North, and possibly in the mountains farther south, litters are produced every other year. Owing to the shorter season of activity in colder regions the time required for the eggs to develop is apparently increased. A similar situation prevails among the vipers of Europe.

RATTLESNAKES ON THE MOVE

Immediately after birth, the young snakes wander extensively. They do not remain with the parent, as the myth concerning snakes swallowing their young for protection would have you believe. Adult snakes are found in greatest abundance during the early spring at the time of the mating season. They may be in search of mates, or their movements may be partly the result of their hunger on coming out of hibernation. Juveniles are more often encountered in numbers shortly after their birth in the autumn.

Dr. Fitch found that the Pacific rattlesnake had no inclination to return to a home site after being removed. On the other hand, some that he marked were found five to nine years later in the general vicinity of the place near the point of capture where they had been released. He found no evidence for any stereotyped pattern of movement, although males tended to remain within restricted areas, nearly a quarter of a mile in diameter. Females moved about less often, commonly remaining within a radius of one-sixth of a mile. Other rattlesnakes had moved distances of over a mile. Any convenient shelter was used during these wanderings—there was no sanctum that might have been called "home". It has been suggested that canebrake rattlesnakes converge to a central denning area from a radius of perhaps twenty miles. This remains to be proved.

HOW LONG DO RATTLESNAKES LIVE?

Rattlesnakes ordinarily do not thrive in captivity. Consequently we can learn little about their normal life span under captive conditions. Information obtained by marking and freeing individual snakes is far more reliable, although the time required for such experiments is usually prohibitive.

The information obtained by Dr. Fitch about the Pacific rattlesnake is better than anything available for other snakes. Dr. Fitch, as we have seen, recaptured several Pacific rattlesnakes in California that had been freed six or seven years previously. Twelve of these were old adults at the time they were first captured and marked for future identification. Most of them must have been adults for at least five or six years prior to capture. Their strings of rattles were of uniform thickness, indicating that those acquired during their early growth had already been lost. Thus, when they were found again after an interval of six or seven years, they must have been adults for at least twelve years. If about four years, the time required to reach the adult stage, be added to this figure, the twelve rattlers recaptured were at least sixteen years old. Probably many of them were much older. It is a fair guess that the life span of the oldest rattler is easily more than twenty years, and possibly thirty.

PRECAUTIONS AGAINST SNAKEBITE

Worry about snakebite is far out of proportion to the potential menace. There is no denying that scores of people are bitten annually. We lack reliable figures for the United States; estimates vary from five hundred to two thousand per year. Over an eight-year period, from 1927 to 1934, fewer than twenty-four hundred cases were actually reported. Fatalities from accidents in the home greatly exceed those from venomous snakes in the United States. It is probable that fewer than five persons in a million are bitten annually. There is greater danger of being struck by lightning than of being bitten by a venomous snake—and a better chance of survival if it is the snake that strikes. With suitable treatment the mortality from the bites of venomous snakes should be less than three out of each hundred people bitten in the United States.

Proper precautions should be taken, nevertheless. In regions infested with venomous snakes it is wise to wear long trousers or full-length boots. Going about barefooted or barelegged can be dangerous. Where the presence of venomous snakes in considerable numbers can be confirmed a suitable kit for supplying first-aid treatment ought to be available.

FIRST AID TREATMENT FOR SNAKEBITE

Prompt treatment of snakebite is essential, not only to reduce the possibility of death, but to ease the pain that usually accompanies such poisoning. Dr. Laurence M. Klauber, whose brilliant work with the rattlesnakes has made them better understood than any other group of snakes in existence, makes the following recommendations:

"Assuming that a person has actually been bitten by a rattlesnake, the following procedure should be adopted by the victim and his companions, if any be present:

"(1) The victim should not become unduly alarmed or excited, and should not run, for to do so will speed up the circulation and the rapidity with which the venom is absorbed. Remember that few cases of rattlesnake bite are fatal.

"(2) Apply a tourniquet between the bite and the heart. This may be a shoestring, necktie, or a rubber band. Rubber tubing makes the best tourniquet. Do not tie it too tightly. Complete stoppage of the circulation is unnecessary and undesirable, but the venous flow should be impeded. Loosen the tourniquet briefly at fifteen-minute intervals.

"(3) With a sharp instrument, such as a razor blade or a knife, make a cross-incision over each fang mark, or connect the two with a single incision. The depth should be about equal to that of the fang, say a quarter of an inch if the snake is of moderate size. Before using, sterilize the cutting instrument if possible, using iodine, alcohol, or the flame of a match.

"(4) Apply suction to the wound and the incisions thus made, either with the mouth or using one of the cupping or suction devices* which have been placed in first-aid kits for this purpose. Apply this continuously for at least half an hour. In a healthy person with good teeth there need be no fear of getting venom into the mouth or stomach with untoward results.

"(5) If antivenin is available, use it in accordance with the instructions accompanying the syringe. However, do not depend upon it as a cure-all. Remember that antivenin and suction are not mutually exclusive; use antivenin if available, but the suction procedure should be carried through in any case.

"(6) If swelling or discoloration progresses up the limb, additional cross incisions should be made above this point and suction should be applied there, the tourniquet having been moved above the swelling. It is best to put on a second tourniquet before removing the first.

"(7) If the patient is faint, give a cup of strong coffee or a teaspoonful of aromatic spirits of ammonia in a glass of water.

"(8) Get the patient to a doctor or hospital as soon as possible, securing a physician experienced in previous snakebite cases if one be available.

"(9) Do not do any of the following things: Do not use potassium permanganate. Do not give whisky. Do not burn or cauterize the wound, since this will interfere with the all-important suction and drainage. Don't use 'folk-lore' remedies; they are a waste of time when time is valuable.

"(10) If the physician in charge of the case has not had previous experience he can secure advice from the United States Public Health Service by wire. The case should be closely watched for the first twenty-four and preferably the first forty-eight hours. Some cases have been lost because the decline in the prominent haemorrhagic symptoms (evidenced by local swelling and discoloration) seemed to indicate

---

* "The rubber-bulb type is probably to be preferred since it will continue its action without an operator."

that the danger was past, to be followed by a sudden and unexpected onset of neurotoxic symptoms. It is suggested that physicians called upon to treat rattlesnake bite, study the publications of the United States Public Health Service, or those of Dr. Dudley Jackson of San Antonio, who has had a wide experience in this field; also the literature accompanying some of the suction devices now on the market in safety-first kits, and the publications accompanying antivenin ampoules contain much useful information. It should be remembered, however, that these directions may be slightly biased as there has been some factional disagreement concerning the relative merits of antivenin and suction. I repeat that antivenin and suction are not mutually exclusive remedies; both should be used extensively in serious cases. The victim should always be typed so that a blood transfusion, if necessary, may be made without delay. Neurotoxic symptoms, frequently involving paralysis of the respiratory centre, call for additional antivenin treatment. The physician will use intravenous injections of glucose and normal salt solution as necessitated.

"The carrying of kits containing suction devices (there are several good ones on the market) is to be recommended to campers, hunters, or others going into rattler-infested country. This is said without any desire to frighten people or to exaggerate the chance of snakebite, which is indeed remote. It is, however, a reasonable insurance precaution."

To conclude our chapters on snakes with a discussion of snakebite might leave a false impression; for, as we have seen, cases of snakebite are not many, and the number of fatal cases is very slight indeed. It is more appropriate to regard the domain of snakes with a feeling of wonder. In this world of fabulous adaptations and everyday miracles, the life of these limbless creatures unfolds with a brooding, mysterious quality that has fascinated man for countless ages.

The cobras and their relatives include some of the largest and most dangerous snakes in existence. The Indian cobra, while by no means the largest, is generally considered the most spectacular member of the family due to its ability to spread the elastic skin of its neck into the familiar "hood". Found throughout most of southern Asia as well as in the Philippines and the Indo-Malayan Archipelago, the Indian cobra is not an aggressive snake and will usually retreat if given the opportunity. This cobra and two African species have specialized fangs which permit them to spit their venom, and they usually aim for the eyes. One drop in the eye causes excruciating pain and if not removed immediately can result in blindness. *See page 1352*

[11-15]

[11-15A]

Coral snakes are the only close relatives of the cobra in the Western Hemisphere, and some not appreciably different types are also found in "cobra country"— Africa, Asia and Australia. The eastern coral snake averages about a yard in length, being near the middle of the size-range of New World varieties. It is found throughout Florida, northward along the coastal plain to North Carolina, and westward along the Gulf Coast to southern Texas and Mexico. Similar species are found in the Southwest, Mexico, and South America. The eastern coral snake feeds mostly on other snakes. *See page 1357*

[11-16]

The four varieties of the copperhead snakes have wide distribution in the United States. The adults are usually less than a yard long, and the eastern variety closely resembles the harmless milk snake. Care should be taken to distinguish the two as the copperhead is definitely dangerous. Like the water moccasin and rattlesnake, the copperhead is a pit viper—the name "viper" applies generally to a widespread family of fanged, poisonous snakes. Copperheads are usually encountered in wooded or rocky areas, and are very versatile in their feeding habits.   *See page 1377*

[11-16A]

With the possible exception of the hooded cobra, no snake has attracted the universal interest and attention accorded the rattlesnake. Found only in the Americas, one variety or another inhabits much of the territory between southern Canada and northern Argentina. The rattle is a string of interlocking segments, a new segment being added each time the skin is shed. The added segments increase in diameter, and strings of 17 or more have been reported. The sound produced resembles the hiss of escaping steam, and a large rattler can be heard 100 feet away. Rattlesnakes range in size from less than two to more than seven feet long, although a length of more than six feet is uncommon. They feed mainly on rodents, but they eat birds, lizards and amphibians.

See page 1379

Vegetables and Flowers

THERE is something about working with earth that is deeply satisfying to boys and girls—and out-of-doors vegetable gardening provides a splendid combination of physical exercise plus the challenge of producing food from the soil.

RADISHES—A FAST CROP

Radishes are a special boon to young gardeners—particularly those with limited planting space. Some radish seeds may be mixed in with seeds of other vegetables, perhaps beets and carrots, for they pop up above ground in a few days. Thus the planted rows are almost immediately marked, and weeds cropping up between them can be dealt with promptly. Another good point about radishes is that they mature in a month or so and can then be pulled out and eaten—while the slower-growing vegetables continue to develop and occupy space vacated by the radishes.

GROWING RHUBARB

Rhubarb will thrive under cooler conditions. A temperature of about 50°F. is suitable; but the atmosphere should be moist and the plants should not be in a draught. To provide an occasional winter pie or breakfast fruit, dig up clumps of rhubarb root in November; you can allow them to freeze under natural conditions or in a freezer. Then store them in a cool place and plant portions from time to time in a box of earth or sand. Tender young shoots will grow from the nourishment stored up in the roots.

MAIZE—A SOMEWHAT PUZZLING PLANT

Many children who have eaten maize cobs as a vegetable would be surprised to know that they come from a grass. The maize plant is American in origin, but will grow in Great Britain, at least in the south. Its common name is Indian corn or sweet corn, but Americans know it so well they refer to it merely as corn.

If a child can start some maize seeds in pots in a warm place they will produce seedlings which can be planted out in May. He will soon see the plants develop if they are kept well watered. The most interesting feature is that the flowers are of two kinds on the same plant: the cobs develop from the spikes of female flowers on the stem, whereas the male flowers grow right at the top of the plant.

Early Development of the Maize Plant. If a child observes the progress of a maize plant, he will see that when it first appears above the ground, its leaves are wrapped in a colourless sheath in a pointed roll. These leaves soon spread apart. Growth is slow; but presently the main stalk becomes visible—and once above the ground, it stretches up rapidly.

The main stem develops more leaves and also ears which are located at the leaf joints, or nodes, where the stalk is hollowed out in order to hold the ear more snugly. The ear is actually on a branch stalk, and the leaves of this stalk are those that are wrapped around the portion we call the "cob". It is on the cob that the seeds, or kernels, will develop.

Flowers—the kind bearing pistils—now appear in pairs along the sides of the cob, and the corn "silk" develops. Each strand of silk is really a pistil, with the stigma at the upper end of a very long style (the prolongation of the ovary). In order to secure pollen, this silk, or pistil, must extend from each flower to the tip of the cob, and beyond the wrapping of the sheath.

How the Maize Plant is Fertilized. Meanwhile large brown tassels have appeared at the top of the main stalk. These are the flowers which bear stamens and produce pollen. The tassel is made up of many florets, each having two anthers hanging from it; half of each anther is a little bag of pollen grains. When the pollen is ripe, this bag opens and the grains fall on the silk far below. The ends of the silk are now branched and covered with fine hairs, to catch the pollen.

After "landing", a pollen grain goes on a remarkable journey— through the entire length of the corn silk until it reaches the ovule. Now that the ovule is fertilized, it will develop into a kernel or seed. If a strand of silk from one of the flowers does not receive a pollen grain, no kernel will develop. An ear with some of these undeveloped kernels is called "imperfect". If pollen from another variety of maize reaches the stigmas of the silk, the ear shows a mixture of the two kinds of kernels.

Self-preservation in the Maize Plant. Corn stalks are so tall and slender that heavy winds can damage them seriously. Yet the structure of the plant provides some defence against wind. The cylinder-like stalk with its pithy centre is sturdier towards the base, as the hard nodes, or joints, occur closer together there. Towards the top the nodes are farther apart, allowing the stalk to bend with the wind and recover.

The root structure also affords protection against the wind. The true roots go deep into the soil, but even so they are inadequate for holding a tall heavy plant upright in a windstorm. However, apart from these roots the plant has other roots about the base—they suggest a tentlike frame—which hold the stalk erect.

PUMPKINS—SOURCE OF DELICIOUS PIES

Another culinary plant, originally American, which is often planted intermixed with maize is the pumpkin. One might suppose that these two vegetables are planted together because one grows high while the other barely rises above the ground. The real reason, however, is found in the nature of the respective roots. The pumpkin is a shallow-rooted plant, whereas the true roots of corn go deep into the earth. The consequence is that the two plants do not fight each other for minerals and water.

The Classic Beauty of the Pumpkin. The fruit of the pumpkin plant, being the source of jack-o'-lanterns and delicious pies, rather over-shadows its flower and foliage. The rugged, broad-based leaves, with their three to five lobes, form a decorative design of classic beauty.

The delicately curved tendril on the pumpkin vine is worth observing. Possibly the tendrils are a holdover from a remote past when pumpkin vines lifted themselves off the ground, as certain gourd vines do today. Occasionally a vigorous pumpkin vine seems to reach out as it climbs over mounds of earth or fences on the edge of a field, as if it were actually a climbing plant.

Pumpkin Seeds. At first a young pumpkin is held up by a stiff stem, but as it grows heavier it rests on the ground. If you cut across a green pumpkin, you will notice that instead of a cavity inside, there are a number of partitions within which seeds are borne. (A cucumber has much the same arrangement.) As the pumpkin ripens, the partitions around the seeds become stringy—a very different texture from the "meat" that forms a thick solid layer between the skin and the inner chamber.

In Great Britain, a child may be able to see marrows or cucumbers growing in a garden. These plants are members of the same family as the pumpkin, and their growth and structure is closely similar.

Weeds Are the Farmer's Enemy

The child who has a chance to work in a garden develops a new respect for Nature and a new understanding. As he comes to realize what skill goes into producing good plants, he may look appreciatively at natural "crops" that no man has aided. He should conclude that although these plants which cover the countryside may be attractive and have certain uses, they are nothing but weeds if they spring up where they are not wanted.

WEEDS—PESTS THAT MAY BE BEAUTIFUL

Children are sometimes perplexed about weeds. We usually speak of them with disdain or annoyance, yet the flowers that some produce are as lovely as those we carefully tend in a garden. It is not the looks of the weeds that disturb us, but their ability to produce fantastic numbers of seeds. This makes them a nuisance in little gardens, and a serious problem to farmers.

Members of the Composite family, which includes daisies and golden-rod, are among the chief offenders; bindweed (convolvulus), couch grass and others swell the ranks. Because of their attractive flowers, many types of weeds have been intentionally transplanted from one part of the world to another. Sometimes a plant which was not a pest in its home environment may escape from cultivation in another country to become a bad weed. Upsetting the balance of Nature is always a risky business.

Flowers That Bloom in Springtime

People in the tropics are fortunate in having flowering plants throughout the year, but few northerners would exchange the joy of seeing the first spring flowers for all the luxury of endless blossoms.

As you venture out into the garden and notice the flowers that appear soon after the last snows have melted, you may wonder how it is that these flowers are on hand in so short a time after the end of cold weather. After all, daisies, irises, and many others will not bloom until summer, and still others—such as asters and chrysanthemums—wait almost until autumn.

Is it only the warm weather that brings forth flowers? If so, why do plants have such varying timetables? Here is the answer: tests have shown that plants react differently to the amount of daylight they receive. Some are stimulated to bloom by short days and long nights.

At first it sounds contradictory to say that anemones and other early spring flowers are "short-day" blossoms—they make their appearance as days are growing longer! However, they have actually been formed *the previous year*. Formation takes place underground; when the temperature becomes favourable, these flowers rise up into the light and air.

When you look at early spring flowers, you are likely to observe that many of them are white. Later in the season you will find more colour. There is a definite reason for this. Flowers formed underground are white to start with because no pigment has been developed. When they are exposed to bright light, many of these flowers take on various hues, among them blue, red, or yellow.

FLOWERS THAT CLOSE FOR THE NIGHT

One of the earliest flowers of spring, the wood anemone must be sought among the decaying foliage of the previous year. As its blossoms grow they rise a matter of inches above the brownish leaves of the year before, and the new leaves may appear very soon after. The petal-like sepals are white or a delicate purple. Young blossoms close during the night and on dark days; older ones remain open all the time.

You are most likely to find the wood anemone, a member of the buttercup family, along the borders of woodlands.

It is quite common in Britain. Its larger cousin, the Pasque-flower, is found only in England, in pastures. It is less common than the wood anemone.

FLOWERS HAVE HIDDEN STOREHOUSES

During February and March, by hedgerows and in shady woods, especially in damp places, a little yellow flower can be found with a circlet of dark, glossy, heart-shaped leaves. This is the lesser celandine, a close relative of the buttercup, which manages to flower so early in the year for a special reason. If you examine its roots you will find a number of club-shaped bodies attached to the base of the plant. These are called tubers; they contained the food stored from the preceding year, and which enabled the plant to start early into growth.

Another plant which comes early into growth in the spring, even in the shady places where it grows, is the bluebell. Bluebells are abundant in Britain; children should easily find plenty of them. The pretty nodding branches of blue flowers often mass together in woodland glades. Each stem of flowers with its circlet of strap-shaped leaves springs from a round juicy bulb beneath the soil. It is the nourishment stored in the fleshy leaves of the bulb which enables the plant to make an early start into growth. New bulbs form from time to time as the older ones die, so a bluebell patch can live on for ever unless some careless human roots up the bulbs when trying to collect the flowers. Once picked, bluebells seldom last very long, but if put into water straight away they make a fine display, gradually darkening in colour.

Do you have crocuses growing in your garden? They have food stores which are similar in shape to bulbs, but are solid, with a covering of thin brown leaves. They are called corms.

VIOLETS

A child who has seen pansies in a garden will easily recognize its wild relatives. The drawing shows the sweetly scented one, which grows by hedgerows and in woods, has broadly heart-shaped blunt leaves and really violet-coloured flowers. It is not very common in Britain; you are more likely to find the many kinds known as "dog-violets".

[A] THE WOOD ANEMONE. Sometimes it is called "windflower" because of the way it sways in the breeze.

[B] THE LESSER CELANDINE. Large numbers can be found together. The petals number anything from eight to twelve.

[C] THE BLUEBELL. Its soft fleshy texture warns you that it will not survive long after picking.

[D] THE SWEET VIOLET. Besides the lovely spring flowers, in summer it bears small greenish flowers beneath its leaves.

The closest relative of the garden pansy is called heartsease. You can tell it by its deeply cut leaves and multi-coloured flowers. Of course, it is much smaller than its cultivated cousin.

Violets survive over the winter by having a thickish brown rootstock called a rhizome from which they bud each year; they may also throw out stems called runners, which produce another plant a little distance away.

CUCKOO-PINT: FLOWERS WITHOUT PETALS

During the summer there can be found under hedgerows all over Britain short, stout, green stems bearing a head of bright glossy red berries. These are the fruits of a plant with lots of romantic names: cuckoo pint, lords-and-ladies, Wake Robin, Jack-by-the-Hedge, and many others.

The flowering spike comes up in the spring; it has a large, tubular, leaf-like part called a spathe, and standing within this a column with a club-shaped (usually dark purple) top. Around the base of the column are many small flowers without petals; the females below, the males above. The spathe is narrowed above the flowers, so you will have to open it out to see them. The constriction is not very narrow, however, because the plant needs the help of the insects which crawl down to the flowers and transfer the pollen from the males to the females of another plant.

Even if the spathe and its spadix, as the column is called, are not up yet, you will be able to recognize the large, triangular, glossy green leaves of the cuckoo pint. They usually have dark irregular blotches on them, but you can hunt for plants with plain leaves or even rarer ones with leaves bearing pale lines along the veins.

CACTUS—NOT JUST A DESERT PLANT

We usually associate cactus plants with the desert. Some cacti, though, thrive in such contrasting localities as the high South American mountains and the coasts of New Jersey.

Many varieties of these hardy, spiny plants have been adopted for indoor gardens, so you don't have to be anywhere near a desert to enjoy the flowers of a cactus. (This ought to interest television-minded children, accustomed to viewing hard-riding cowboys among desert

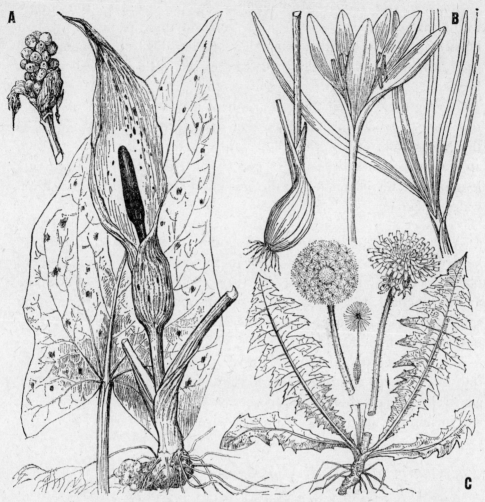

[A] CUCKOO-PINT. The flies which fertilize the petalless flowers are temporarily trapped in the base of the spathe.

[B] THE CROCUS. Several sorts are cultivated in gardens, and a few have escaped to adorn the meadows.

[C] THE DANDELION. On the right of the drawing is a flower head at the height of blooming. On the left is a flower head gone to seed.

scenes!) Cacti may bloom in your home any time during the year—not just in the spring as the desert plants do.

In fact, cacti with their rather ugly bodies often bear very beautiful flowers with very many brightly coloured petals. Even the prickly pear, which became such a bad weed when introduced into Australia, can delight the eye with its pink, yellow or rose-coloured blooms.

Storehouses of Water. Most children are fascinated by the curious forms that cacti take. They can see some of these plants in the hothouses of botanical gardens, and they are very likely to wonder about their lack of leaves. Actually the cacti are able to do very well without leaves.

"Leaf-green" in their thick fleshy stems makes possible the manufacture of their food, and the absence of leaves prevents the water inside the plants from evaporating. They store water in the stems to such an extent that they can survive periods of drought for an amazingly long time. Many people lost in the desert owe their lives to these natural water tanks.

Plant Survival in the Desert. In humid regions plant species are largely assured of survival by their great numbers. In deserts, where plants are comparatively sparse, they have evolved a number of defences to keep humans and animals from preying on them. Notable are the spines, thorns, and toughness of the cactus. Other plants depend on bitterness or unpleasant odours, a few on poison.

Although a cactus can manage on very little water and in poor sandy soil, this does not mean you should starve your house-grown ones. To get the best results they should have as good a soil as you can give them, and in summer, when they are growing strongly, a watering every day.

The Charm of Summer Blossoms

DANDELIONS—PERSISTENT WEEDS

This golden-headed flower, one of the most persistent of all weeds, is occasionally a source of income to youngsters, who earn money by helping rid lawns of dandelions. In early summer dandelions can provide a lot of fun for children. The youngsters can whistle through the hollow stems, or make dandelion curls of them; they may even pretend to tell time by the number of puffs required to blow away all the seeds on a ripened stem.

The Adaptable Dandelion. Children have done such things to dandelions for ages, man has tried his best to exterminate them, animals have grazed on them, other plants have attempted to crowd them out—all in vain. The dandelion has had extraordinary success in surviving. One of the many reasons for its survival is its adaptability to circumstances. For example, in a meadow of tall grasses the plant sometimes reaches a height of two feet—and more; but on a lawn the flower stem may be less than two inches tall, saving the flower head from the blades of the lawn mower!

The Dandelion is a Composite Flower. The dandelion belongs to the great family group that we call "composites"—a word that comes from the Latin and means "made up of parts". Apart from the dandelions, the composites include asters, thistles, and a great many other kinds of flowers. All have compound flower heads (the term "head" is used for a close cluster of flowers).

Petals and Buds in the Composites. Some of the composites have a disc in the middle of the flower head. This disc is made up of tiny tubular florets, and around it are brightly coloured ray flowers, or "petals".

The dandelion belongs to another type of composite which has a petal-like part on each flower. In a just-opened dandelion you can see the buds at the middle all curving slightly toward the centre. They are also shorter and a darker yellow than the outer florets, for they are younger. The flower head is well protected by long bracts; shorter bracts near the stem curl back, forming a frill.

How the Dandelion Opens and Closes. Dandelions close on dark days and at night. It is often eight o'clock before they begin to wake up, and it may take a full hour for the golden head to be completely opened. When all the florets on a head have blossomed, the dandelion closes for good until its seeds are formed. Each seed is equipped with a fluffy parachute-like head. When this head is dry it can "parachute" the seed to new growing ground.

How the Dandelion Got Its Name. You need a good imagination to see that the notched edges of dandelion leaves resemble lions' teeth; but that is what they looked like to someone in France who named the plant *dent-de-lion*, whence we get our name for it.

FROM "DAY'S EYE" TO DAISY

This flower, which has much in common with the dandelion, is a great favourite with children. Like the dandelion, it is an amazingly persistent weed; and it is also a composite. At its centre we find numerous short, yellow, tubular disc flowers.

These are surrounded by twenty or more ray flowers—"petals" to children, who love to pull them off one by one with "he loves me, he loves me not". If you look closely at these ray flowers you will see that each has a pistil which shows a two-part stigma at its apex. The flowers ripen many seeds but they lack the travelling equipment of the dandelion.

In the yellow garden daisy commonly called "black-eyed Susan", the purple-brown disc flowers form a conical, button-like centre for the orange ray flowers. Still more colour is added to the flower when brilliant orange pollen appears.

Like the dandelion, the daisy opens in the morning. It owes its name to this habit—people in Old England called it "day's eye", which finally became our "daisy".

BUTTERCUPS—SOMETIMES THREE FEET HIGH

Growing as they do in the same fields, buttercups and daisies are commonly associated in children's minds. There is an essential difference, however; whereas the daisy is a composite, the buttercup is a single flower. The five (and sometimes more) wedge-shaped petals are slightly curved, giving the flower its cup-like form.

"Do You Like Butter?" The bright yellow colour of the buttercup gives it a shiny finish which in bright sunlight quite easily reflects on another surface. That is why the answer is nearly always positive when a child follows the old custom of holding a buttercup under a playmate's chin to see if he "likes butter". (If yellow is reflected on the chin, the answer is "yes".) Outside the reflecting petals are five sepals, about half the length of the petals and pale yellow with brownish tips.

There are many different kinds of buttercups; the common tall one of pastures and meadows is properly called Buttercup. It may grow as tall as three feet! Though you are likely to find buttercups as early as May, they bloom through August and sometimes until frost appears.

LUCKY CLOVER

Among our most popular superstitions is the one that promises good luck to the finder of a four-leaf clover. It is a fact, however, that the clover plant is good fortune for all of us.

25,000 to the Inch. In addition to being a valuable food crop for horses and cattle, clover has an almost magical way of bringing fertility to the soil. The secret of this power lies in the little swellings—sometimes called root tubercles or nodules—that you will find on the rootlets. Each swelling is occupied by bacteria, so many that 25,000 of them, lined up, would cover only an inch of space.

These bacteria extract nitrogen, a valuable chemical fertilizer, from the soil and change its form so that clover can absorb it. When a crop of clover is harvested, the roots remain in the ground with their precious supply of fertilizer. This is one reason why farmers, in rotating their crops, plant clover every few years.

Collecting Clovers is Fun. It is fun for a child to make a collection of clovers, for there are many attractive species, including crimson, red, white, hare's foot, zigzag, and yellow. Both leaves and blossoms can be kept for several years when pressed between pieces of wax paper or cellophane. It is even possible to become an expert at finding the rare four-leaf clover to add to one's collection. These leaves turn up here and there in the midst of stalks with three leaflets.

The three-leaved grouping is the customary one and has given the plant its scientific name, *trifolium* ("three-leaved"). To find the out-of-the-ordinary stalk with four leaflets, you need to practise looking for a *square* pattern in a carpet of *triangles*. Stand erect and scan the clover design; where one four-leaf specimen is found there are apt to be more.

A FAMILY OF CHARACTER

A group of plants you can soon learn to recognize is that with four petals arranged in a cross. The wallflower and the stock are members of it, so you should not have far to go to find an example. Take a flower apart and look for the six stamens and the pistil with its two points at the top. Outside the coloured petals are four sepals, two flat and two boat-shaped.

[A] THE OX-EYE DAISY. The yellow disc and white rays betray this tallish composite even to a fleeting glance from a railway train.

[B] THE BUTTERCUP. It is sometimes called "crow's foot" because the shape of its leaf suggests a bird's claws.

[C] RED CLOVER. It has an unusually long period of blooming. Flowers may be found from April until November.

[D] LADY'S SMOCK. A plant which only sets seed when cross-fertilized.

Once you can spot the cross-like petal structure you will be able to find lots of other plants which, though they differ in many other ways, all have this flower type in common. Many vegetables, like cabbage, kale and turnip, produce examples if you leave them to flower. Watercress is another of the family, and on a garden rockery you may find others: sweet alyssum and white or purple rockcress.

Now go out into the countryside and look for more. The plants may not be large, but that makes the hunt worth while. One that flowers nearly all the year round and is common on rough ground everywhere is the shepherd's purse, which has a string of white flowers and toothed leaves. On the stalk beneath the flowers are the triangular pods which give the plant its name. In meadows and pastures, you should look for the handsome little plant called lady's smock, or cuckoo-flower; it has pinkish-tinged flowers and lower leaves divided into rows of leaflets. Along hedgerows you may find Jack-by-the-hedge, with its small white flowers and large rounded lower leaves. It is also called garlic mustard or sauce-alone, and if you crush its leaves and smell them, you'll find out why.

WILD CARROT—BEAUTIFUL YET TROUBLESOME

This plant is quite large, delicate, and handsome, but it is also a very troublesome weed. You are likely to find it in waste places and fields almost anywhere, but more especially near the sea, and it is really closely related to the garden carrot. On a fully grown plant, the yellowish root is six inches long or more; but it isn't good to eat.

The Flower Cluster. Each large flat flower cluster, with its radiating pattern as fine as lace, is made up of many small flower clusters, each in turn with a stalk of proper length to fit into just the right place in the medallion pattern. These small flower clusters each have twenty or thirty tiny white blossoms in a rosette design.

If you look down at one of the large flower clusters, you will notice that the outside blossoms have small bracts—the special leaves which, in this case, resemble the petals. These are larger than the petals and create a pleasing border effect for the complete cluster. Often you find a single wine-coloured floret in the centre on its own stalk.

When the flower cluster begins to wither, each of the small clusters curves inward until the whole unit suggests a tiny bird's nest. Thousands of fruits develop on each plant, and many live to germinate.

GOLDENROD—ANOTHER COMPOSITE FLOWER

From early summer to autumn you can see these bright yellow flowers on dry, sandy roadsides, along riverbanks and near seashores, at the edges of woods, in meadows; even in mountainous regions. In all these localities grow varying forms of goldenrod; the same species is found all over Europe.

The goldenrod is another interesting example of a composite flower. Each flower head is very small, but the plant makes a bright showing because the florets are set close together. On each delicate branch there is a procession of ray flowers with short but brilliant banners, and a few tubular disc flowers that open out like bells. Look at the disc flowers closely and you will see in them the pollen tubes or yellow two-part stigmas.

The garden goldenrod came to us long ago from North America where many other kinds also occur wild.

ASTERS—ATTRACTIVE TO BEES

Like goldenrod, asters also came to our gardens from North America, and there are numerous species. They too are composites, but the flower heads are different in form from the goldenrod. At the centre of their circular flower heads there are yellow disc flowers that may turn a dull purplish colour as they age.

These disc flowers yield an abundance of nectar, and you frequently see bees, small butterflies, and beelike flies visiting them.

Some asters (Michaelmas daisies) produce masses of blooms from the same rootstock year after year. Because of their popularity with gardeners they have been developed by interbreeding into many beautiful varieties.

They bloom late in the summer just when a fresh burst of colour is needed.

SOME SUNFLOWERS ARE TWELVE FEET HIGH

The sunflower, giant of the flower garden, is not so commonly planted as it used to be. Curiously, the tallest wild sunflower, which grows up to twelve feet tall in swamps in North America, has a head only about two inches across. If you grow some garden sunflowers, the huge "flower" will give you an ideal example of a composite head to examine.

First to unfold are the wide, flaring ray flowers that are largely responsible for the sunflower's spectacular appearance. There may be two or three rows of these. When they are a few days old, you can see inside them a circle of florets from which ripened pollen and stigmas have already disappeared. Below the florets fertilized seeds are now developing.

Inside this circle is another composed of florets where coiled-back stigma lobes protrude from the anther tubes. Next, moving toward the centre of the flower head, you may see several rows of florets in which pollen is just being pushed out; and within this ring may be florets with the anther tubes still closed. At the centre are buds with the inmost few still covered with the green spear points of their bracts, or specialized leaves.

Sunflower Myths. Children who have not had a chance to observe sunflowers may be interested to know if it is true that these blossoms twist on their stems in order to face the sun all day. This widely circulated story is charming but not particularly accurate. Some of these giant flowers have been observed turning with the sun to a certain extent when they first unfold—but not after they grow heavy with seeds.

Another published observation is that many turn for their last few weeks of bloom to the east and remain that way. Watching those that grow in my neighbour's garden—they are planted, by the way, to raise seeds for winter bird-feeding—I have not seen any evidence of the flower heads following the sun. The direction they usually face is south.

Wild-flower Bouquets and Gardens

Part of the joy of flowers comes from picking them and arranging them in enchanting bouquets. Unfortunately, we are limited for the most part to garden plants. Many wild plants are so rare that it is unfair to deprive other people of the joy of finding them. Others, though plentiful, do not survive long removed from their roots.

WHAT FLOWERS TO CHOOSE

Despite these limitations, we still have some excellent material for wild-flower bouquets. Do not take too many different kinds. Limit

[A] WILD CARROT. These flowers grouped in lacy geometric designs, seem especially suitable for decorations in "modern" settings.

[B] GOLDENROD. This is the wild goldenrod of the country lane and river bank, a smaller flower than the garden variety.

[C] THE ASTER. This beautiful garden flower is usually called "Michaelmas daisy" because it blooms near Michaelmas day.

[D] THE THISTLE. Another plant with flowers in heads—but here the flowers are all tubular and bluish.

yourself to several which go well together. Small flowers can look delightful in a shallow container. Remember to take some foliage to set off the blooms and, if the flowers are not brightly coloured, put them in a plain vase, which they can dominate.

When you have a chance to pick wild flowers, it is best to cut them with scissors or regular garden clippers. Later, the stems should be cut on a slant with a sharp knife. Then, if they are left in a pail of water for a few hours or overnight, they may regain much of their freshness.

WILD FLOWERS IN THE GARDEN

Many plants which are rare in Britain have become so because in the past people could not resist the temptation to transplant them into their gardens. This was especially foolish because rarity in the wild is usually due to some special circumstance which is not easily copied in a garden. If you do want to bring wild flowers into your garden, take one plant only from where many grow; take a good ball of soil with the root, and plant in the same degree of light or shade.

How to Press and Mount Plants

Pressing wild flowers is still another way in which children can get pleasure from them. They can also have a world of fun arranging the flowers in attractive groupings and framing them as wall pictures. You will again want to stress to youngsters, before they do any picking, that only plants that are plentiful should be taken. We live on a small island where everyone is in reach of the countryside. The flowers can bring joy to all, but only if people refrain from taking the rarer ones for themselves alone.

Techniques for Pressing Flowers. When you collect plants for pressing, keep them damp until you are ready to place them under pressure. You can manage this by taking a few damp newspapers on a collecting trip and carrying the plants between the pages. For ease of handling, you can roll up the papers—not too tightly, however, or the leaves may crack.

When you are ready for pressing, place a piece of newspaper about twelve by eighteen inches on the floor, and lay plants or flowers on top of it. As you may want to mount them later on, take care to arrange petals, and leaves in natural positions. A violet, for example, usually looks more natural if pressed in profile. A few buds with the full-bloom flower and some leaves make a complete story and an interesting composition. Make sure that no plants overlap during the pressing.

How to Dry Out Plant Moisture. Now that you have laid out the plants on newspaper, cover this arrangement with a layer of newspaper equal in thickness to the thickest part of the plant or plants below. Add layers of plants and paper until your entire collection is arranged in this way. Over this pile, place a board or other flat object equal in size to the newspaper, and on top of this put weights such as books, rocks, or other heavy things. If the weight is not heavy enough, the plants will wrinkle.

Change the paper or move the plants to a dry place every day for at least four days—then less often, for about ten days. The more rapidly the plant loses its moisture, the better its delicate colours will be preserved.

How to Mount Plants. To mount a plant you need a piece of glass as large as the specimen you are preparing. Cover the glass with a thin coating of glue diluted a bit with a drop or two of vinegar. Place the dried plant on the glue (to get the glue on one side), then quickly transfer the plant to a piece of mounting paper. Now you are ready for framing. If a plant is too delicate for this treatment—it may curl when it is picked up from the glue—you can mount it by placing thin strips of gummed paper at intervals across the stem.

Some Plants Have No Green Parts

Knowing as we do how vital "leaf-green" is to the growth of plants, the mushroom and other fungi that develop without a trace of green seem rather mysterious to us. No wonder that generations ago, when not too much was known about plant life, people stood in superstitious awe of the magic "toadstools", which seemed to spring out of nowhere and were sometimes good food and sometimes poisonous. When you are on a woodlands hike with your youngster, especially in late summer or autumn, you can get a lot more out of your trip if you watch for members of this fungus family growing wild.

WHAT FUNGI FEED ON

Lacking "leaf-green", fungi are unable to manufacture starch and sugar, and some absorb them from dead wood, withered leaves, or soils enriched by remains of plants. They are the kind of fungi we know as "saprophytes" (living on dead or decaying matter), and they are valuable plants because they prevent forests from becoming choked with dead wood. As mushrooms and other fungi absorb tissue from stumps and old logs, the wood softens and falls apart.

FUNGI THAT PREY ON LIVING THINGS

The other kinds of fungi, the "parasites", take their food from the cells of living things. These fungi are often dangerous enemies to the plants and animals on which they grow. It is a parasitic fungus that causes "potato blight"; another is responsible for the costly disease known as "wheat rust". The simplest forms of living things that take their nourishment from animals are the bacteria that cause diphtheria, typhoid fever and other serious diseases.

MUSHROOMS DISPERSE SPORES INSTEAD OF SEEDS

As mushrooms have no flowers, a child may wonder what they do about seeds. Flowerless plants have their own special kind of "seed". Microscopic in size, it is called a "spore". After landing in a favourable growing place, the spore of a mushroom develops rapidly into a thread-like form. From this a whole mass of threads grow out for weeks or even months, until there is enough tissue to produce a fruiting body —then, with startling suddenness, the mushroom itself appears!

PRECAUTIONS AGAINST POISONOUS MUSHROOMS

Mushrooms and toadstools are usually abundant in damp, wooded spots, as they do not need sunshine. If we happen to be in one of these localities, we may be tempted to pick some mushrooms suitable for eating. *It is a temptation best denied.* Unfortunately some people rely on tests that are supposed to indicate when a species is poisonous— they believe toadstools turn a silver spoon black or change colour when bruised.

None of these tests is known to be of the slightest value. A number of characteristics do help to distinguish the poisonous from the non-poisonous species, but only an expert should attempt to draw the distinction for eating purposes.

Better to beware; some fungi are *deadly*.

Mosses Favour Moist Places

There is a shrub known as the "flowering moss", but you can be sure it is not really moss—no moss bears flowers. The so-called flowering moss merely suggests moss in a superficial way.

Mosses, like mushrooms, produce spores. The moss spore grows a branched green thread on which leafy buds soon appear. They develop further into leafy stems which in turn produce rootlike projections—not true roots. Some of the plants bear eggs at their leaf tips while others produce sperms. Wind, or films of water supplied by rain or dew, may bring sperm and egg together. After fertilization they develop delicate upright stalks on which spore cases full of green-coloured spores will form.

THE MOSS AS A COMPASS

In June you can generally see mosses in all stages of development. Usually you find moss only in rather moist places, on woodland floors and on rocks and tree trunks where strong sunlight does not penetrate. The American Indians commonly used this bit of nature lore to determine their direction—moss usually grows on the northern side of tree trunks where there is least exposure to sunlight.

A MOSS TO LOOK FOR

An easy moss to recognize because of its large size is hair moss. This grows in tufts on sour soil in damp places, not only in woods but in grassy fields and meadows. It and its relatives grow all over Europe, Asia and North America. It is rather a large moss with stems a foot long, and in autumn you will see it as a greenish-brown mass of stems.

By the arrival of summer the new growth tips these with vivid green. During dry spells the small leaves shut lengthwise into mere threads and huddle against the stem to prevent their moisture from evaporating. After a rain they open up again. In the past this moss was used for making small brooms and for mattresses.

Ferns, Fronds, and "Fiddle Heads"

Most children love ferns as much as they do flowers. Ferns lack coloured petals, but by way of compensation they have gracefully shaped fronds, or leaves, that are a delight to the eye from the time they come through the ground and uncoil like a watch spring until the divided leaves are fully developed. While the leaves are still partly coiled they are called "fiddle heads", as their shape resembles the top of a violin.

FERNS FOR DECORATION

Ferns are frequently cultivated and used for decoration; consequently a fernery makes a very rewarding project. To begin with, the ground for a fern garden should be dug up and treated with well-rotted leaves and humus. When you transplant specimens from the woods, take a large ball of earth with each plant, and water the ferns well for several days after each planting. Give the ferns the same conditions of shade and sunshine, as far as possible, as they had in the natural state.

You will surely find the lady fern with its delicate much divided fronds, and spores in small curved lines beneath. Another common one is hart's-tongue fern, with its unique undivided frond.

FERNS AND THEIR SPORES

Ferns, like the mosses and mushrooms, produce spores, Most ferns also have a creeping underground stem, called a "rootstock", which pushes forward and sends up new fronds each year. One species is known as the "walking fern" because new growth is started where the tips of the fronds come in contact with ground or rocks.

If you have read the sections on plants in these volumes with interest, and have taken the trouble to look for the examples mentioned, you may want to know more about the subject. Before you choose a book which describes or illustrates a lot more plants, go to your local library and examine some of those available. You need to select carefully to get one at the correct level—neither too advanced nor too superficial.

You will need to learn more of the general subject—botany—too. Find a textbook with sections on physiology, ecology and morphology. Try to understand what it would feel like to be a plant struggling to live. Remember that plants are not merely objects in the world: each is a link in the long chain of evolution which makes up the plant kingdom.

You may find that your interest will deepen into a real study. You will be ready to obtain Clapham, Tutin and Warburg's *Flora of the British Isles* and make a full study of the plants of our islands. The ultimate object of such study is that you may come to sense the profound reality of the harmony in diversity which the evolution of plant life shows. And because all life, including our own, has depended, and still depends, on the ability of plants to survive and multiply, knowledge of plant evolution can be a part, at least, of a philosophy of life—a source of great emotional satisfaction.